GEOLOGICAL SOCIETY OF AMERICA
SPECIAL PAPERS
NUMBER 2

FOSSIL CRUSTACEA
OF THE
ATLANTIC AND GULF
COASTAL PLAIN

BY

MARY J. RATHBUN

PUBLISHED BY THE SOCIETY

1935

WAVERLY PRESS, INC.
BALTIMORE, MD.

The Special Papers
of
The Geological Society of America
are made possible
through the bequest of
Richard Alexander Fullerton Penrose, Jr.

CONTENTS

CONTENTS

ILLUSTRATIONS

PLATES

FIGURES

INTRODUCTION

STATEMENT OF THE PROBLEM

LITTLE has been published concerning the fossil Crustacea of eastern and southern United States. The United States Geological Survey and the United States National Museum have been gradually accumulating specimens, but the sum total is moderate. Crustacean remains, compared to molluscan, are scarce. The shells are thin, fragile, and easily destroyed, so that the remains consist largely of chelae or parts of chelae, as these are usually thicker than the carapace and other appendages. The number of species at hand is relatively small; more are known from the lower Cretaceous of Texas and the Midway of Alabama than elsewhere.

In the Cretaceous the predominating genera of shrimp-like forms are *Hoploparia* and *Callianassa*; the former belongs to the family, Homaridae, best known from the common lobster; the latter is a burrowing shrimp of a type which persists at the present day to a limited extent but which in ancient times was noted for the great number of species and individuals. The largest crustacean here recorded occurs in the Comanche series of Texas, a *Palaeastacus* figured on Plates 3–5. Several species of the genus *Linuparus* of the family Palinuridae indicate the derivation of Recent *L. trigonus* of Japan. The three pagurids, or hermit crabs, are referred to genera now living. A prevailing genus of true crabs is *Necrocarcinus*, a Calappid which became extinct after the Eocene. Fairly abundant are the Gymnopleura or Raninidae, representatives of which still persist in the waters bordering the Coastal Plain. Notable is the presence of two isopods, Aegidae, rare among fossils.

In the Eocene the genus *Ischnodactylus* prevails over *Hoploparia* in the Homaridae; the Callianassidae, the Palinuridae, and the Raninidae are well represented, and the number of crabs is considerably increased.

Very little material is at hand from the Oligocene and the Pliocene. Of the 26 species found in the Miocene, 12 are Recent, also. An interesting addition is *Lobonotus foerstei* from the greensand layer of Gay Head, Massachusetts, whence the naturalists, William Stimpson (1863) and later Alpheus S. Packard (1900), each described a new species of crab.

The Stomatopoda are represented by two species, both Recent, one in the Miocene, the other in the Pleistocene.

SOURCES OF MATERIAL

The United States Geological Survey and the United States National Museum have furnished the bulk of the material used. Next in importance is the collection, loaned by W. S. Adkins, Bureau of Economic Geology, University of Texas, of a large number of specimens from the Comanche series of the Cretaceous, which are, with few exceptions, new to science. Other important collections are those from the Florida State Geological Survey (E. H. Sellards); the Alabama Museum of Natural History (T. H. Aldrich); Johns Hopkins University (E. W. Berry and R. Lee Collins); the Academy of Natural Sciences of Philadelphia (H. A. Pilsbry); the New Jersey State Museum (H. B. Kümmel); the Staten Island Institute of Arts and Sciences (Charles W. Leng); the Portland Society of Natural History (Arthur H. Norton); the University of Texas[1] (F. L. Whitney); and the California Oil Company, Colorado, Texas (John E. Adams).

The writer is indebted to Dr. T. W. Stanton, Dr. L. W. Stephenson, Dr. J. B. Reeside, Dr. W. C. Mansfield, and Dr. Julia Gardner for assistance in the preparation of this report, and to Mr. W. O. Hazard and Miss Frances Wieser for their care in the making of illustrations.

The area included in this paper extends from southwestern Maine (Pleistocene) and New York (Cretaceous) to southern Texas (Cretaceous).

UNUSUAL EXTENSIONS OF RANGE

A number of the Coastal Plain species have been found also in the interior of the continent. Of Cretaceous forms, *Dakoticancer overana*, in the Cliffwood clay of New Jersey and the Ripley of Tennessee, was originally described from the Pierre shale of South Dakota. *Tetracarcinus subquadratus* of the Gulf series of New Jersey has been taken from the Lewis shale of Wyoming, and *Necrocarcinus pierrensis* from the Woodbury clay of New Jersey and the Pierre shale of South Dakota.[2] *Linuparus vancouverensis*, first known from the Nanaimo group of the Lower Cretaceous of Vancouver Island, was later found in the Denison group of Oklahoma. *L. canadensis*, of the Benton group of Alberta and South Dakota, reappears in the Ripley formation of Tennessee and the Eagle Ford of Louisiana. *Zanthopsis errans* Woods, described from the Clavilithes series of Peru, re-appears, if one can judge from an isolated claw, in the lower Claiborne of Mississippi.

MINGLING OF CRETACEOUS WITH EOCENE

One of the largest collections examined is that made by L. C. Johnson, of the United States Geological Survey, in 1883 while exploring the Midway of Wilcox County, Alabama. It embraces the Prairie Creek region, the Pine Barren section, and Allenton. There the Sucarnoochee clay rests

---

[1] The Adkins collection is in the Bureau of Economic Geology.

[2] Similar parallel occurrences of other invertebrates are fairly common. For example, Reeside [J. B. Reeside: *The Cephalopods of the Eagle sandstone and related formations in the western interior of the United States*, U. S. Geol. Surv., Prof. Pap. 151 (1927)] notes the occurrence of *Scaphites hippocrepis* (p. 23) and *S. similis* (p. 25) in New Jersey as well as in Montana and Wyoming.

upon the Selma chalk of the Cretaceous; "the formation consists chiefly of tough clay, which is dark gray to black when moist but when dry is light gray and breaks into roundish lumps with conchoidal fracture."[3] As the fossil materials of the two formations were mostly loose from the matrix and had freely mingled, it was necessary to make a more or less arbitrary separation. The specimens of the Cretaceous genera, *Enoploclytia* and *Palaeastacus*, are assigned to the Selma formation and the balance to the Midway. *Ischnodactylus*, not before recorded from the Eocene, is now known from the Jackson formation of Mississippi as well as the Midway of Alabama. Of other genera common to Cretaceous and Eocene, there is collateral evidence that *Linuparus* and *Callianassa* occur in the Sucarnoochee of Alabama; *Hoploparia*, *Raninella*, *Xanthilites*, and *Panopeus* are ranged there with a reservation.

CORRELATION WITH EUROPEAN FORMS

One of the most striking examples of close relationship with the European fauna is the existence in the Comanche series of Texas of the gigantic *Palaeastacus walkeri* (Whitfield) which resembles the type species of the genus, *P. sussexiensis* (Mantell) from the Senonian of England. The Goneplacid, *Plagiolophus bakeri* n.sp., lower Claiborne, Texas, is much like Bell's type species, *P. wetherelli*, from the Londinian of northern Europe. The genus, *Caloxanthus* A. Milne Edwards (Cenomanian, France), is now known from the Comanche of Texas; and *Hepatiscus* is represented in the Midway of Alabama by a species allied to Bittner's *H. pulchellus* from the Lutetian of the Venetian Alps.

NEW ADDITIONS

Three new genera, *Prehepatus*, *Ophthalmoplax*, and *Scyllarella*, have been found necessary, the last named represented also in Europe by two long known species.

[3] Special Report No. 14, Ala. Geol. Surv. (1926) p. 255.

LIST OF SPECIES AND DISTRIBUTION

CRETACEOUS

DECAPODA

Penaeidae
Penaeus wenasogensis Rathbun
Glypheidae
Glyphea (?) *carolinensis* Rathbun
Meyeria mexicana Rathbun, n.sp.
Erymidae
Enoploclytia sculpta Rathbun
Enoploclytia tumimanus Rathbun, n.sp.
Enoploclytia wenoensis Rathbun, n.sp.
Enoploclytia (?) sp.
Eryma (?) *americana* Rathbun
Eryma flecta Rathbun
Eryma stantoni Rathbun, n.sp.
Palaeastacus walkeri (Whitfield)
Palaeastacus kimzeyi Rathbun, n.sp.
Palaeastacus selmaensis Rathbun, n.sp.
Homaridae
Hoploparia gabbi Pilsbry
Hoploparia gladiator Pilsbry
Hoploparia tennesseensis Rathbun
Hoploparia mcnairyensis Rathbun
Hoploparia georgeana Rathbun, n.sp.
Hoploparia dentonensis Rathbun, n.sp.
Hoploparia blossomana Rathbun, n.sp.
Hoploparia tarrantensis Rathbun,
    n.sp.
Ischnodactylus texanus Rathbun, n.sp.
Nephrops americanus Rathbun, n.sp.
Family undetermined
Macruran undetermined
Callianassidae
Callianassa mortoni Pilsbry
Callianassa mortoni var. *punctimanus*
    Pilsbry
Callianassa sp. indet.
Callianassa cretacea Rathbun, n.sp.
Callianassa aquilae Rathbun, n.sp.
Callianassa pilsbryi Rathbun, n.sp.
Callianassa oktibbehana Rathbun, n.sp.
Callianassa valida Rathbun, n.sp.
Callianassa bosqueana Rathbun, n.sp.

Palinuridae
Linuparus kleinfelderi Rathbun
Linuparus canadensis (Whiteaves)
Linuparus vancouverensis (Whiteaves)
Linuparus adkinsi Rathbun, n.sp.
Linuparus (?) sp.
Linuparus (?) sp.
Archaeocarabus (?) *whitfieldi* (Pilsbry)
Paguridae
Paguristes ouachitensis Rathbun, n.sp.
Pagurus banderensis Rathbun, n.sp.
Petrochirus taylori Rathbun, n.sp.
Dakoticancridae
Dakoticancer overana Rathbun
Dakoticancer overana australis Rath-
    bun, n.subsp.
Tetracarcinus subquadratus Weller
Dynomenidae
Graptocarcinus texanus Roemer
Xanthosia aspera Rathbun, n.sp.
Xanthosia wintoni Rathbun, n.sp.
Dromiidae
Dromia (?) *anomala* Rathbun, n.sp.
Calappidae
Necrocarcinus oklahomensis Rathbun,
    n.sp.
Necrocarcinus pierrensis (Rathbun)
Necrocarcinus graysonensis Rathbun,
    n.sp.
Necrocarcinus texensis Rathbun, n.sp.
Necrocarcinus (?) sp.
Prehepatus cretaceus Rathbun, n.sp.
Prehepatus pawpawensis Rathbun,
    n.sp.
Raninidae
Notopocorystes punctatus Rathbun,
    n.sp.
Notopocorystes parvus Rathbun, n.sp.
Notopocorystes (?) *ripleyensis* Rathbun,
    n.sp.
Raninella testacea Rathbun

4

Raninella mucronata Rathbun, n.sp.
Raninella (?) *armata* Rathbun, n.sp.
Raninella (?) *starkvillensis* Rathbun, n.sp.
Notosceles bournei Rathbun
Atelecyclidae
Avitelmessus grapsoideus Rathbun
Portunidae
Ophthalmoplax stephensoni Rathbun, n.sp.

Ophthalmoplax comancheensis Rathbun, n.sp.
Xanthidae
Actaea cretacea Rathbun, n.sp.
Caloxanthus americanus Rathbun, n.sp.
Menippe cretacea Rathbun, n.sp.
Majidae
Stenocionops primus Rathbun, n.sp.

ISOPODA

Aegidae
Palaega guadalupensis Rathbun, n.sp.

Palaega williamsonensis Rathbun, n.sp.

EOCENE
DECAPODA

Homaridae
Hoploparia johnsoni Rathbun, n.sp.
Ischnodactylus cookei Rathbun, n.sp.
Ischnodactylus cookei lowei Rathbun, n.subsp.
Ischnodactylus cultellus Rathbun, n.sp.
Ischnodactylus (?) *dentatus* Rathbun, n.sp.
Ischnodactylus (?) sp.
Nephropsis midwayensis Rathbun, n.sp.
Callianassidae
Upogebia midwayensis Rathbun, n.sp.
Callianassa alpha Rathbun, n.sp.
Callianassa alpha var. Rathbun, n.var.
Callianassa beta Rathbun, n.sp.
Callianassa gamma Rathbun, n.sp.
Callianassa delta Rathbun, n.sp.
Callianassa epsilon Rathbun, n.sp.
Callianassa alabamensis Rathbun, n.sp.
Callianassa ulrichi C. A. White
Callianassa ulrichi claibornensis Rathbun, n.subsp.
Callianassa hulli Rathbun, n.sp.
Callianassa brazoensis Stenzel
Callianassa wechesensis Stenzel
Palinuridae
Linuparus texanus Rathbun, n.sp.
Linuparus wilcoxensis Rathbun, n.sp.
Archaeocarabus (?) *gardnerae* Rathbun, n.sp.
Scyllaridae
Scyllarella gibbera Rathbun, n.sp.

Scyllarella aspera Rathbun, n.sp.
Paguridae
Paguristes johnsoni Rathbun, n.sp.
Pagurus alabamensis Rathbun, n.sp.
Dromiidae
Dromilites americana Rathbun, n.sp.
Leucosiidae
Hepatiscus americanus Rathbun, n.sp.
Raninidae
Raninoides ovalis Rathbun, n.sp.
Notosceles bournei Rathbun
Raninella eocenica Rathbun, n.sp.
Symethis johnsoni Rathbun, n.sp.
Symnista bidentata Rathbun, n.sp.
Calappidae
Calappilia diglypta Stenzel
Xanthidae
Menippe burnsi Rathbun, n.sp.
Menippe jacksonensis Rathbun, n.sp.
Menippe anomala Rathbun, n.sp.
Ocalina floridana Rathbun
Harpactocarcinus americanus Rathbun
Harpactocarcinus mississippiensis Rathbun, n.sp.
Harpactocarcinus rathbunae Stenzel
Harpactocarcinus sp. Stenzel
Zanthopsis errans Woods
Zanthopsis carolinensis Rathbun, n.sp.
Zanthopsis peytoni Stenzel
Zanthopsis peytoni var. *parva* Stenzel
Xanthilites alabamensis Rathbun, n.sp.
Panopeus estellensis Rathbun, n.sp.
Galenopsis americana Rathbun, n.sp.

Xanthidae, gen. and sp. undetermined
Goneplacidae
Plagiolophus bakeri Rathbun, n.sp.

Majidae
Stenocionops suwanneeana Rathbun, n.sp.

OLIGOCENE

DECAPODA

Callianassidae
Callianassa berryi Rathbun, n.sp.
Callianassa vaughani Rathbun
Raninidae
Ranina georgiana Rathbun, n.sp.

Portunidae
Callinectes alabamensis Rathbun, n.sp.
Necronectes vaughani Rathbun, n.sp.

MIOCENE

DECAPODA

Callianassidae
Callianassa floridana Rathbun, n.sp.
Callianassa matsoni Rathbun, n.sp.
Callianassa suffolkensis Rathbun, n.sp.
Callianassa atlantica Rathbun
Callianassa vaughani Rathbun
Paguridae
Petrochirus inequalis Rathbun
Petrochirus bouvieri Rathbun
Paguristes chipolensis Rathbun, n.sp.
Calappidae
Calappa flammea (Herbst)
Leucosiidae
Persephona punctata (Linnaeus)
Portunidae
Portunus (Portunus) sayi (Gibbes)
Portunus, sp.
Callinectes sapidus Rathbun

Necronectes drydeni Rathbun, n.sp.
Scylla floridana Rathbun, n.sp.
Cancridae
Cancer borealis Stimpson
Cancer irroratus Say
Cancer proavitus Packard
Xanthidae
Menippe floridana Rathbun, n.sp.
Menippe nodifrons Stimpson
Lobonotus foerstei Rathbun, n.sp.
Panopeus herbstii Milne Edwards
Eurytium limosum (Say)
Goneplacidae
Archaeoplax signifera Stimpson
Majidae
Euprognatha, sp.
Libinia emarginata Leach
Libinia dubia Milne Edwards

STOMATOPODA

Chloridellidae
Gonodactylus oerstedii Hansen

PLIOCENE

DECAPODA

Paguridae
Petrochirus bouvieri Rathbun
Xanthidae
Menippe nodifrons Stimpson
Panopeus herbstii Milne Edwards

Eurytium limosum (Say)
Parthenopidae
Parthenope (Platylambrus) charlottensis Rathbun

PLEISTOCENE

DECAPODA

Homaridae
  Homarus americanus Milne Edwards
Callianassidae
  Callianassa atlantica Rathbun
Calappidae
  Calappa flammea (Herbst)
Leucosiidae
  Persephona punctata (Linnaeus)
Portunidae
  Callinectes sapidus Rathbun
Cancridae
  Cancer irroratus Say

Xanthidae
  Panopeus herbstii Milne Edwards
  Menippe mercenaria (Say)
Ocypodidae
  Ocypode albicans Bosc
  Uca pugnax (Smith)
  Uca subcylindrica (Stimpson)
Majidae
  Hyas araneus (Linnaeus)
  Libinia emarginata Leach
  Libinia dubia Milne Edwards

STOMATOPODA

Chloridellidae
  Chloridella empusa (Say)

The geographic and the stratigraphic distribution of the species are shown on the accompanying Tables *1* to *6*.

TABLE 1.—*Geographic and Stratigraphic Distribution of Cretaceous Species*

GULF SERIES
  New York
    Merchantville clay marl
      Linuparus kleinfelderi

  New Jersey
    Monmouth
      Tinton beds
        Callianassa mortoni
        Tetracarcinus subquadratus
      Redbank (red sand)
        Callianassa mortoni
      Navesink marl (lower marl)
        Callianassa mortoni
      Antenna of Palinurid
    Matawan
      Wenonah sand
        Callianassa mortoni
      Woodbury clay
        Callianassa mortoni
        Tetracarcinus subquadratus
        Necrocarcinus pierrensis
      Merchantville clay marl
        Hoploparia gabbi
        Hoploparia gladiator
        Callianassa mortoni
      Palm, undetermined
    Magothy: Cliffwood clay
      Tetracarcinus subquadratus
      Dakoticancer overana
    Upper Cretaceous
      Formation unknown
        Archaeocarabus (?) *whitfieldi*
    First bed greensand
      Callianassa mortoni

  Delaware
    Monmouth
      Callianassa mortoni
      C. mortoni var. *punctimanus*
      "*Astacus sp.*"
    Matawan
      Hoploparia gabbi
      Hoploparia gladiator
      Callianassa mortoni
      Callianassa sp. indeterminate

  Maryland
    Monmouth
      Hoploparia georgeana
      Callianassa mortoni
      C. mortoni var. *punctimanus*

GULF SERIES—*Continued*
  Maryland—*Concluded*
    Matawan
      Callianassa mortoni

  North Carolina
    Peedee
      Eryma (?) *americana*
      Avitelmessus grapsoideus
    Black Creek: Snow Hill calcareous
      marl
      Glyphea (?) *carolinensis*

  South Carolina
    Peedee
      Ophthalmoplax stephensoni

  Georgia
    Eutaw (?)
      Callianassa mortoni

  Tennessee
    Ripley
      Enoploclytia sculpta
      Eryma flecta
      Hoploparia tennesseensis
      Hoploparia mcnairyensis
      Callianassa mortoni
      Linuparus canadensis
      Dakoticancer overana
      Raninella testacea
      Avitelmessus grapsoideus
      Penaeus wenasogensis (lower
        Ripley)
    Selma
      Avitelmessus grapsoideus

  Alabama
    Ripley
      Eryma stantoni
      Callianassa mortoni
      Avitelmessus grapsoideus
      Ophthalmoplax stephensoni
    Selma
      Enoploclytia tumimanus
      Palaeastacus selmaensis

  Mississippi
    Ripley
      Hoploparia tennesseensis
      Callianassa mortoni

TABLE 1—*Continued*

GULF SERIES—*Continued*
Mississippi—*Concluded*
Ripley—*Concluded*
Callianassa pilsbryi
Linuparus (?) sp.
Dakoticancer overana australis
Notopocorystes (?) *ripleyensis*
Avitelmessus grapsoideus
Ophthalmoplax stephensoni
Selma
Callianassa oktibbe- ⎫
hana ⎪
Raninella (?) *stark-* ⎬ Oktibbeha
villensis ⎪ tongue
Avitelmessus grap- ⎪
soideus ⎪
Menippe cretacea ⎭
Callianassa mortoni
Enoploclytia (?) sp.

Louisiana
Eagle Ford
Callianassa aquilae
Linuparus canadensis

Arkansas
Nacatoch sand
Callianassa mortoni
Paguristes ouachitensis
Brownstone marl
Stenocionops primus

Texas
Navarro
Palaega williamsonensis
Notosceles bournei
Dakoticancer overana australis
(chalky marl member)
Ophthalmoplax stephensoni
Taylor marl
Palaeastacus kimzeyi (base of
Wolfe City sand member)
Petrochirus taylori (base of Wolfe
City sand member)
Palaega guadalupensis
Austin chalk
Palaega guadalupensis
Eagle Ford
Callianassa aquilae

GULF SERIES—*Continued*
Texas—*Continued*
Woodbine
Menippe cretacea
Crab, undetermined
Anacacho limestone
Callianassa mortoni
Blossom sand
Hoploparia blossomana

Wyoming
Lewis shale
Tetracarcinus subquadratus

South Dakota
Pierre shale
Dakoticancer overana
Necrocarcinus pierrensis
Carlile, upper Benton
Linuparus canadensis

Alberta
Benton shale
Linuparus canadensis

British Columbia
Nanaimo group
Linuparus vancouverensis

COMANCHE SERIES
Texas
Buda
Palaeastacus walkeri
Graptocarcinus texanus
Pawpaw
Ischnodactylus texanus
Nephrops americanus
Callianassa cretacea
Linuparus (?) sp.
Xanthosia wintoni
Necrocarcinus texensis
Necrocarcinus (?) sp.
Prehepatus pawpawensis
Ophthalmoplax comancheensis
Actaea cretacea
Caloxanthus americanus
Weno
Enoploclytia wenoensis
Palaeastacus walkeri

TABLE 1—*Concluded*

COMANCHE SERIES—*Continued*
   Texas—*Continued*
      Denton
         Hoploparia dentonensis
         Hoploparia tarrantensis
         Ischnodactylus texanus
         Macruran, undetermined
         Callianassa cretacea
         Callianassa valida
         Linuparus adkinsi
         Xanthosia aspera
         Xanthosia wintoni
         Dromia (?) *anomala*
         Necrocarcinus graysonensis
         Necrocarcinus texensis
         Notopocorystes punctatus
         Notopocorystes parvus
         Raninella mucronata
         Raninella (?) *armata*
      Fort Worth
         Palaeastacus walkeri
         "Lobster related to *Homarus*"

COMANCHE SERIES—*Continued*
   Texas—*Concluded*
      Duck Creek
         Ischnodactylus texanus
         Prehepatus cretaceus
         Ophthalmoplax comancheensis
      Goodland
         "Indeterminate limb segments"
      Comanche Peak
         Callianassa bosqueana
      Glen Rose
         Pagurus banderensis

  Oklahoma
      Denison group: "Marietta"
         Linuparus vancouverensis
         Necrocarcinus oklahomensis

  Mexico
      Cuchillo shale
         Meyeria mexicana

TABLE 2.—*Geographic and Stratigraphic Distribution of Eocene Species*

North Carolina
  Jackson group
    Castle Hayne marl
      Menippe burnsi
      Menippe anomala

South Carolina
  Santee limestone, basal Jackson
    Menippe burnsi
  Claiborne group
    Zanthopsis carolinensis

Florida
  Ocala limestone
    Ocala floridana
    Stenocionops suwanneeana

Alabama
  Jackson group
    Harpactocarcinus mississippiensis
  Midway group
    Sucarnoochee beds
      Ischnodactylus cookei
      Ischnodactylus cultellus
      Ischnodactylus (?) sp.
      Hoploparia johnsoni
      Nephropsis midwayensis
      Upogebia midwayensis
      Callianassa alpha
      Callianassa beta
      Callianassa gamma
      Callianassa delta
      Callianassa epsilon
      Callianassa alabamensis
      Callianassa ulrichi
      Linuparus wilcoxensis
      Archaeocarabus (?) *gardnerae*
      Scyllarella gibbera
      Scyllarella aspera
      Paguristes johnsoni
      Pagurus alabamensis
      Dromilites americana
      Hepatiscus americanus
      Raninoides ovalis
      Notosceles bournei
      Raninella eocenica
      Symethis johnsoni
      Symnista bidentata
      Xanthilites alabamensis

Alabama—*Concluded*
  Midway group—*Concluded*
    Sucarnoochee beds—*Concluded*
      Panopeus estellensis
      Galenopsis americana
      Xanthidae, genus and species
        indeterminate

Mississippi
  Jackson group
    Ischnodactylus cookei lowei
    Callianassa alpha var.
    Menippe jacksonensis
    Harpactocarcinus mississippiensis
  Claiborne group
    Callianassa ulrichi claibornensis
    Harpactocarcinus americanus (lower)
    Zanthopsis errans
  Lower Eocene
    Ischnodactylus cultellus
    Ischnodactylus (?) *dentatus*

Louisiana
  Claiborne group
    Harpactocarcinus americanus

Arkansas
  Midway group
    Callianassa ulrichi
    Callianassa hulli
    Notosceles bournei

Texas
  Claiborne group
    Cook Mountain formation
      Callianassa brazoensis
      Calappilia diglypta
      Harpactocarcinus americanus
      Harpactocarcinus rathbunae
      Harpactocarcinus species
      Plagiolophus bakeri
    Mount Selman formation
      Callianassa wechesensis
      Zanthopsis peytoni
      Zanthopsis peytoni var. *parva*
  Midway group
    Linuparus texanus (lower Midway)
    Dromilites americana
    Notosceles bournei

TABLE 3.—*Geographic and Stratigraphic Distribution of Oligocene Species*

VICKSBURG GROUP	VICKSBURG GROUP—*Concluded*
Georgia	Alabama—*Concluded*
Glendon limestone	Glendon limestone
Ranina georgiana	*Ranina georgiana*
Florida	Mississippi
Marianna limestone	Glendon limestone
Necronectes vaughani	*Callianassa berryi*
	Necronectes vaughani
Alabama	
Byram marl (?)	Mexico
Callinectes alabamensis	Upper Oligocene
	Callianassa vaughani

TABLE 4.—*Geographic and Stratigraphic Distribution of Miocene Species*

Massachusetts
  Greensand layer
    Cancer proavitus
    Lobonotus foerstei
    Archaeoplax signifera

Maryland
  Choptank formation
    Necronectes drydeni
  Calvert
    Cancer irroratus

Virginia
  Yorktown (upper part)*
    Callianassa suffolkensis
    Callianassa atlantica
  Yorktown (lower part)*
    Cancer borealis
  Yorktown
    Persephona punctata
    *Callinectes sapidus**
    Panopeus herbstii
    *Libinia dubia**
  Calvert (probably)
    Panopeus herbstii

North Carolina
  Yorktown (upper part)
    *Callianassa atlantica**
  Yorktown (Duplin)
    Persephona punctata
    Panopeus herbstii
    *Eurytium limosum**
  Yorktown
    Persephona punctata†
    *Panopeus herbstii**
  St. Marys
    Gonodactylus oerstedii
  Formation not given
    Libinia emarginata

South Carolina
  Upper Miocene (horizon?)
    Persephona punctata

Florida
  Upper Miocene
    Petrochirus bouvieri
    Euprognatha sp.
  Upper part of Middle Miocene
    Choctawhatchee formation
      Calappa flammea
      Menippe floridana
      Menippe nodifrons
  Middle Miocene
    Alum Bluff group
      Shoal River formation
        Calappa flammea
      Oak Grove sand
        Calappa flammea
  Lower Miocene
    Alum Bluff group
      Chipola formation
        Callianassa floridana
        *Callianassa matsoni***
        Petrochirus inequalis
        Paguristes chipolensis
        Calappa flammea
        Portunus (P.) sayi
        Callinectes sapidus
        Menippe nodifrons
        Eurytium limosum
    Tampa limestone
      Callianassa matsoni
      Portunus, sp.
      Scylla floridana

Mexico
  Lower Miocene
    Callianassa vaughani

* Horizon according to W. C. Mansfield.
† Horizon uncertain.
** Hawthorn formation according to C. W. Cooke.

TABLE 5.—*Geographic and Stratigraphic Distribution of Pliocene Species*

North Carolina	Florida
Waccamaw formation	Caloosahatchee marl
Panopeus herbstii	*Petrochirus bouvieri*
Eurytium limosum	*Menippe nodifrons*
	Parthenope (Platylambrus) charlottensis

TABLE 6.—*Geographic and Stratigraphic Distribution of Pleistocene Species*

New Brunswick	Maryland—*Concluded*
Leda clay	Talbot formation—*Concluded*
Homarus americanus	*Callianassa atlantica*
	Cancer irroratus
Maine	*Panopeus herbstii*
Leda clay	*Chloridella empusa*
Cancer irroratus	
Hyas araneus	Virginia
	Pleistocene†
Massachusetts	*Callinectes sapidus*
Pleistocene†	
Callinectes sapidus	North Carolina
Panopeus herbstii	Pamlico formation
	Persephona punctata
Connecticut	Pleistocene†
Pleistocene†	*Callinectes sapidus*
Homarus americanus	
	South Carolina
New Jersey	Sandy beds
Cape May formation	*Calappa flammea*
Callinectes sapidus	*Persephona punctata*
Cancer irroratus	*Callinectes sapidus*
Panopeus herbstii	*Menippe mercenaria*
Uca pugnax	Pleistocene†
Libinia emarginata	*Panopeus herbstii*
Libinia dubia	
	Florida
Delaware	Pleistocene†
Talbot formation	*Ocypode albicans*
Uca pugnax*	*Cancer irroratus*
Maryland	Texas
Talbot formation	Pleistocene†
Callinectes sapidus*	*Uca subcylindrica*

* Pamlico.
† Exact horizon unknown.

TABLE 7.—*Formations in which Tertiary crustaceans occur*

	Massachusetts	Maryland	Virginia	North Carolina	South Carolina	Georgia	Florida	Alabama	Mississippi	Louisiana Arkansas Texas
Pliocene				Waccamaw			Caloosahatchee			
Miocene	Greensand of undetermined formation	Choptank	Yorktown; Calvert (probably)	Yorktown; St. Marys	Upper Miocene		Upper Miocene; Choctawhatchee; Shoal River; Oak Grove; Chipola; Tampa; Alum Bluff			
Oligocene (Vicksburg)						Glendon	Marianna	Byram (?)	Glendon	
Eocene				Jackson (Castle Hayne)	Basal Jackson (Santee); Claiborne		Ocala	Jackson; Midway (Sucarnoochee)	Jackson; Claiborne	Claiborne (Cook Mountain); Midway

TABLE 8.—*Formations in which the Cretaceous crustaceans occur*

Series	New York	New Jersey	Delaware Maryland	North Carolina South Caroline	Georgia	Alabama Mississippi Tennessee	Arkansas Louisiana	Texas	Oklahoma	Wyoming	South Dakota	Canada	Mexico
UPPER CRETACEOUS (GULF SERIES)		Monmouth: Tinton, Redbank, Navesink	Monmouth	Peedee		Ripley-Selma¹	Nacatoch	Navarro			Pierre		
	Merchant-ville	Matawan: Wenonah, Woodbury, Merchant-ville	Matawan	Black Creek			Browns-town	Taylor-Anacacho		Lewis		Benton in Alberta Nanaimo in British Columbia	
		Magothy			Eutaw (?)			Austin-Blossom					
							Eagle Ford²	Eagle Ford			Carlile		
							Woodbine		"Mari-etta"				
LOWER CRETACEOUS (COMANCHE SERIES)								Buda, Pawpaw, Weno, Denton, Fort Worth, Duck Creek, Goodland, Comanche Peak, Glen Rose, Travis Peak					Cuchillo³

¹ Oktibbeha tongue is at top of Selma.
² In deep wells only in Louisiana.
³ Of Travis Peak age.

DETAILED DESCRIPTION OF GENERA AND SPECIES

CRETACEOUS

Phylum ARTHROPODA
Class CRUSTACEA
Order DECAPODA

Family PENAEIDAE
Genus PENAEUS Fabricius
Penaeus wenasogensis Rathbun

1926. *Penaeus wenasogensis.* Rathbun, *in* Bruce Wade, U. S. Geol. Surv., Prof. Pap. 137, p. 185, pl. 63, figs. 1–6, 8–11.

Occurrence: Tennessee: State Line cut, near Wenasoga, Miss.; "between Selma and Ripley formations" (probably lower Ripley), Upper Cretaceous.
Collections: Vanderbilt University (type), U. S. National Museum.

Family GLYPHEIDAE
Genus GLYPHEA von Meyer
Glyphea (?) *carolinensis* Rathbun

1923. *Glyphea* (?) *carolinensis.* Rathbun, N. C. Geol. and Econ. Surv., vol. 5, p. 407, pl. 102, figs. 1–3.

Occurrence: North Carolina: Black River, near Ivanhoe, Sampson County, 56¼ miles above Wilmington; upper part (Snow Hill calcareous member) of Black Creek formation (type-locality).
Collection: U. S. National Museum; type, Cat. No. 31897.

Genus MEYERIA McCoy
Meyeria mexicana Rathbun, n.sp.

(Plate 26, figures 1–4)

The margins are chiefly embedded in hard rock as is also the anterior end. A little in front of the deep nuchal furrow there are visible three prominent, narrow, longitudinal ridges which converge gradually forward; the outer pair have small flattened denticles, the median ridge is blunt and has a single granule near the middle (of the exposure). Behind the nuchal furrow the carapace has been compressed and cracked out of shape; the median line shows evidence of low granulation; on either side there is a blunt ridge beginning not far behind the cervical suture, curving upward and backward and bearing a few scattered granules; it meets a straight line which has a single row of granules on two-thirds of its length, and is directed backward and slightly upward. Near its posterior end, another granulated ridge begins and runs straight outward and backward nearly to the posterior margin. Adjacent to these two ridges are scattered punctae of variable size. The lower half of the carapace is covered with separated granules, visible to the naked eye.

Little of the abdominal pleura is exposed. The pleura of the second to fifth articles, inclusive, of the abdomen overlap slightly each succeeding segment; the tips (so far as exposed) are rounded, the amount of overlap diminishing from segment 2 to 5; there is a row of three or four granules on the pleura of segments 2 and 3; sixth segment longest, third next.

Measurements: Length of exposed carapace, 32.7 millimeters; of abdomen, 36.6 millimeters.

Relation: Compared to *M. magna* McCoy[4] of Europe, the telson is much shorter, devoid of a transverse, anterior furrow and almost smooth, without the fine granules of *magna*. The granulated ridge on the posterior lateral carapace slants more downward and backward. *M.? harveyi* Woodward[5] from the Upper Cretaceous of Vancouver has never been figured and is too briefly described to compare with the Mexican form.

Occurrence: Mexico: Chihuahua, Abuja Colorada canyon on north side of Cerro Chino, 26 kilometers northwest of Cuchillo Parado. Cretaceous; lower part of a thick section of the Cuchillo shales of Burrows, Dufrenoya zone, Gargasian formation (upper Aptian) = Travis Peak formation, approximately. Robert E. King and W. S. Adkins, collectors.

Collection: Peabody Museum, Yale University; type.

Family ERYMIDAE

Genus ENOPLOCLYTIA McCoy

Enoploclytia sculpta Rathbun

1926. *Enoploclytia sculpta*. Rathbun, *in* Bruce Wade, U. S. Geol. Surv., Prof. Pap.
137, p. 187, pl. 66.

Occurrence: Tennessee: Dave Weeks place, Coon Creek, McNairy County; Ripley formation, Upper Cretaceous (type-locality).
Collection: U. S. National Museum; type, Cat. No. 73119.

Enoploclytia tumimanus Rathbun, n.sp.

(Plate 1; Plate 2, figures 1-5)

Carapace semicylindrical, narrowing forward, irregularly tuberculate, interspaces covered with punctae or sockets opening obliquely forward and outward; it is divided longitudinally by a narrow median sulcus which bifurcates on the anterior part of the carapace to enclose the mesogastric lobe, which is narrow, almost linear, and terminates posteriorly at a short

---

[4] F. McCoy: *On the classification of some British fossil crustacea, with notices of new forms in the University Collection at Cambridge,* Ann. Mag. Nat. Hist., ser. 2, vol. 4 (1849) p. 334.

[5] Henry Woodward: *Further note on podophthalmous crustaceans from the Upper Cretaceous formation of British Columbia,* Geol. Mag., n.s., dec. 4, vol. 7 (1900) p. 434.

distance in front of the hepatic furrow. This furrow is broad and deep, its two halves nearly straight, the outer portion nearly vertical in profile, the dorsal portion directed backward, forming a very obtuse angle at the middle. The cervical furrow is equally deep and parallel with the hepatic on the side of the carapace, but dorsally it is shallower and runs far back, forming an acute angle at the middle; a shallow secondary furrow is present on the dorsum behind the cervical and subparallel to it. A short curved furrow near the margin of the carapace connects the hepatic and cervical furrows. The tubercles are mostly large, especially on the side in front of the hepatic suture. The posterior half of the carapace is dorsally flat and roughened with punctae but with few spines.

Merus of cheliped compressed, increasing in thickness toward distal end, longitudinal margins each with two convergent rows of stout tubercles or spines; there is also a row which nearly encircles the distal end. Carpus short, stout, rounded. Manus stout, about 1¾ times as long as wide, thickest in the middle, without marginal lines; cross-section in small specimens round, in large specimens slightly oval, the diameter in the plane of the fingers being the greater. Both carpus and manus have a number of large tubercles arranged mostly in irregular rows; the lower surface of the manus is less rough, having a longitudinal row of about ten small tubercles just above the lowest point of the inner surface. Only fragments of fingers remain. The basal cross-sections are round and equal. Fingers long, gradually tapering to a slender tip which is curved in two different planes, one toward the opposing finger and the other in a direction at right angles; surface coarsely punctate; a prehensile edge is formed by a single row of short, cylindrical, cone-tipped spines of varying sizes, the larger spines separated by from two to ten smaller ones.

The material on which this species is based is fragmentary. Of several hundred pieces, four are recognizable as carapaces, and one shows the narrow mesogastric region; hands are numerous, wrists, arms, and fingers less numerous. No pieces of the abdomen are recognizable. The ornamentation of punctae and tubercles is sufficient to identify small fragments.

Measurements: Greatest width of largest carapace (type-specimen) 40 millimeters. Length of a detached palm, 31.4 millimeters; width of same (in plane of fingers), 20.3 millimeters; thickness, 18.4 millimeters. Length of largest palm, 60 millimeters; greatest width, 32 millimeters.

Relation: In carapace and chelipeds this species has a strong resemblance to E. leachii (Mantell)[6]; it has a longer and narrower merus, a manus more swollen in the middle.

Occurrence: Taken by L. C. Johnson at three stations, 264, 281, and 284, in the vicinity of Prairie Creek, Allenton and Pine Barren section,

[6] Astacus leachii Mantell. G. A. Mantell: The fossils of the South Downs (1822) p. 142, 221, pl. 29, figs. 1, 4 and 5; pl. 30, figs. 1 and 2; pl. 31.

Wilcox County, Alabama; probably Selma Chalk.   An original label for 284 gives, "Scattered shells and fragments picked up on prairies," Sections 32 and 34, Township 12, Range 10, April 25, 1883.   The type-specimen belongs in this lot.[7]

Arroyo Castaño, State of Coahuilla, Mexico; about 2 miles northwest of the Blessé Ranch.   Horizon, a greenish glauconitic soft limestone of highest Escondido (= High Maestrichtian) age.   W. F. Cummins, W. Kennedy, and J. M. Sands, collectors.

Collection: U. S. National Museum; type, Cat. No. 73799.   University of Texas; Mexican specimens.

Enoploclytia wenoensis Rathbun, n.sp.

(Plate 6, figures 7, 8)

Represented by abdominal segments 1–6 and by the hinder end of the carapace.   Carapace exceeding considerably the abdomen in width and rough with flattened granules of irregular size.   Abdomen smooth, without furrows, covered with rather large, separated punctae; the sixth segment appears to be the longest (its hinder end is much broken), the fifth the shortest; that portion of the first segment normally concealed by the carapace is now exposed.   The pleura of the fourth and the fifth segments are to be seen; their margins are arcuate and converge to a point.   Length (approximate) of six abdominal segments, 34 millimeters.

Occurrence: Texas; Gainesville, Cooke County, in brickyard pit; Weno, Lower Cretaceous; 1919; W. S. Adkins, collector.

Collection: University of Texas; type, Coll. No. 191.

Enoploclytia (?) sp.

(Plate 2, figure 6)

A convex fragment covered with tubercles similar to those of *E. granulicauda* Schlüter.[8]

Occurrence: Mississippi: Cut of Southern Railway, 3 miles southeast of Corinth, Alcorn County; Selma chalk; 1909; L. W. Stephenson, collector (6460).

Collection: U. S. National Museum, Cat. No. 73842.

Genus ERYMA von Meyer
Eryma (?) *americana* Rathbun

1923. *Eryma* (?) *americana*.   Rathbun, N. C. Geol. and Econ. Surv., vol. 5, p. 406, pl. 102, figs. 5–7.

Occurrence: North Carolina: Neuse River, 34⅔ miles above New Bern, Craven County; Peedee formation.
Collection: U. S. National Museum; type, Cat. No. 31899.

---

[7] Unless otherwise stated, the catalogue numbers are those of the United States National Museum.   Numbers in parentheses indicate those used by the senders.

[8] C. Schlüter: *Neue und weniger gekannte Kreide- und Tertiär-Krebse des nördlichen Deutschlands*, Zeitschr. d. deutschen Geol. Ges., vol. 31 (1879) p. 599, pl. 14.

Eryma flecta Rathbun

1926. *Eryma flecta*. Rathbun, *in* Bruce Wade, U. S. Geol. Surv., Prof. Pap. 137, p. 188, pl. 63, figs. 7, 13–15.

Occurrence: Tennessee: Half a mile northwest of Gravel Hill, McNairy County; "Selma-Ripley formations" (probably Ripley).
Collection: U. S. National Museum; type, Cat. No. 73115.

Eryma stantoni Rathbun, n.sp.

(Plate 5, figure 12)

Holotype, a right chela, with perhaps the mate to it alongside. Palm a little longer at middle than its width. Proximal margin almost at right angles to upper and lower margins, which are slightly convex. Surface covered with a dense network of fine broken ridges running crosswise of the palm. Fixed finger broad at base occupying half the height of the palm and tapering steadily to a point; a sharp carina runs through the middle of its length and is continued a short distance on the palm; lower margin punctate; directly above the margin a row of distant punctae. Between the carina and the prehensile margin there is an irregular line of granules in the proximal part. Dactylus narrower at its insertion than the opposing finger, retaining its width for the proximal half, then gradually diminishing to the tip. Minor manus about three-fourths as large as major, and similar; fixed finger not exposed.

Measurements: Length of palm at middle, 21.4 millimeters; height at middle, 17.7 millimeters; length of fixed finger along the gape, 16 millimeters.

Relation: This specimen has a strong resemblance to Wood's *Eryma* sp.[9]

Occurrence: Alabama: Chattahoochee River, 12 miles below Eufaula; Ripley formation, Upper Cretaceous; T. W. Stanton, collector.

Collection: U. S. National Museum; type, Cat. No. 73790.

Genus PALAEASTACUS Bell
Palaeastacus walkeri (Whitfield)

(Plate 3, figures 7–9; Plate 4; Plate 5, figures 1–5; Text-figure 1)

1880. *Paramithrax ? walkeri*. Whitfield, *in* C. A. White, U. S. Geol. Surv. Terr. for 1878, 12th Ann. Rept. (separate, 1880) p. 37, pl. 16, fig. 1*a–c*, pl. 17, fig. 1*a*.
1905. *Paramithrax ? walkeri*. Schuchert, U. S. Nat. Mus., Bull. 53, p. 484.
1913. Crustacean indet. (possibly *Paramithrax*). Whitney, Texas Acad. Sci., Tr. for 1910 to 1912, vol. 12, p. 27, pl. 13, fig. 3.
1928. *Paramithrax ? walkeri*. Adkins, Univ. Texas, Bull. 2838, p. 83.

The holotype has not been located. Dr. Whitfield's description was made from a plastotype such as exists in the United States National Museum. A text figure (no. 1) bearing his name is in the same Museum; its proportions are inaccurate

---

[9] H. Woods: *A monograph of the Fossil Macrurous Crustacea of England*, Palaeont. Soc. London, Mem., vol. 80, 1926 (1928) pl. 19, fig. 6.

in comparison with the plastotype, the palm being too long, but the figure is published for the detail of the surface.

The following is adapted and condensed from Whitfield's description:

This species is represented only by the right chela and part of the wrist. The manus is robust and somewhat triangular in transverse section. Length of hand to base of fixed finger bears the proportion to the height and thickness, exclusive of spines, that 7 does to 5 and 4. Both fingers are rounded, without flattening or carination, gently and nearly evenly curved throughout their length. Hand angular on outer surface below the middle, a little more flattened inside. Carpus strong, obliquely ovate and provided with a large flattened basal projection near the inferior articulation. Surface of specimen marked by numerous strong conical tubercles which may have been spines; they are arranged in longitudinal lines on the

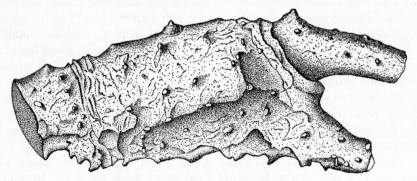

FIGURE 1—*Palaeastacus walkeri*

Holotype, right chela and wrist

outer side of the manus and partly so on the inner; but on the inside there is also a line of large nodes extending obliquely downward from the upper edge parallel to the margin of the socket of the dactylus and at a short distance from it and continuing on the fixed finger. The carpus is also marked by lines of strong spines; a double transverse line on the inside parallel to the distal margin and divided from it by a broad rounded channel; a single row of stronger spines outside; the flattened area forming the basal projection of the article is also bordered by spines. The surface between spines is wrinkled, as shown in a drawing by Whitfield made from the holotype itself.

To the above it may be added that the row of spines near the middle of the inner surface of the palm is oblique and directed toward the middle of the articulation with the dactyl; also that the fixed finger is bent downward and distinctly inward, the movable one only slightly inward; the fingers of the holotype so narrow and widely separated at base, are indicative of great length.

Additional specimens: One specimen from Shoal Creek is a left chela showing the distal two-thirds of the manus and a pair of long fingers lacking only the extreme tips. The outer layer of shell is absent, but enough of the characteristic coarse spines are present on the inner surface of the palm to serve for identification. The distal two-thirds of the fingers is compressed laterally. The basal half of an additional finger (right dactyl) shows an irregular row of small, unequal spines along the prehensile margin.

A large carapace from Tarrant County has been flattened by bending along the median line or is perhaps a cast shell; it measures fully 17.5 centimeters long and 11 centimeters from middle to lateral edge of carapace.   It is covered with well-separated tubercles, smaller in lower half of carapace, larger and more prominent or spinose above; on either side close to the middle line, a row of stout spines directed obliquely forward; one of these is 9 millimeters long on upper margin and 3 millimeters wide at base.   The carapace is crossed by two deep sutures; the cervical groove crosses the median line at about the anterior third of carapace and extends obliquely downward and forward in a sinuous course, near the middle of which it bends forward; at this point there is, in front of it, a deep triangular depression; in the hepatic region the groove curves forward to the margin.   The branchio-cardiac groove is subparallel to the cervical through the greater part of its length, but at the hepatic region proceeds directly downward; toward the median line it inclines strongly backward until near the middle, whence it continues to the posterior margin.   The hepatic region is longitudinally oblong with the anterior end narrowed and produced to a point; the groove on its upper border is broad and shallow and widens proximally into a triangular depression where it joins the branchio-cardiac groove.   A deep and wide groove just in front of posterior margin of carapace.

Measurements: Holotype, length of palm at middle, 80.2 millimeters; height of same at middle, 55.4 millimeters; thickness at middle, 44 millimeters; horizontal diameter of section of dactylus, 14 millimeters.

Relation: The type claw has a strong resemblance to that of the type species of the genus, *P. sussexiensis* (Mantell) = *P. dixoni* Bell,[10] but the armature of the latter is much closer and heavier.

Occurrence: Texas: Lower Cretaceous: Tarrant County, 2½ miles southeast of Fort Worth at crossing of Houston and Texas Central and International Great Northern tracks in Sycamore Creek valley, near small waterfall; basalmost stratum of Weno; 1919; W. S. Adkins (201); one large carapace (U.T.).

Williamson County, one mile north of Georgetown, cliffs on Georgetown-Belton road; Fort Worth limestone; April 19, 1930; W. S. Adkins; left cheliped with part of manus, carpus, and merus (U.T.).

Shoal Creek, 29th Street, Austin, Travis County; Buda limestone (Whitney); one chela showing fingers and half the palm (U.T.).

San Antonio, Bexar County; Cretaceous (formation unknown); Mrs. N. S. Walker, collector; one chela with wrist; plastotype, Cat. No. 8360.

Collections: U. S. National Museum, University of Texas; type not located.

Palaeastacus kimzeyi Rathbun, n.sp.

(Plate 2, figures 15–21)

Two relatively small specimens of the right manus with only a short stump of the dactylus.   Compared to *P. walkeri* they are less rotund, somewhat shorter, and their inner and outer surfaces are squarer, much as in Bell's figure of a small *P. sussexiensis*.[11]   The arrangement of spines is similar to that of *P. walkeri*, but their number is greater, small spines or perhaps tubercles being numerous and well separated.   The general surface is wrinkled between the accidentally truncated spines.   The larger specimen (holotype) has a deep longitudinal furrow on either side just below the upper margin, which is unnatural, as in the smaller specimen it is a shallow furrow.   A pair of spines is placed transversely above the dactylus near its base.

[10] See F. Dixon: *The geology and fossils of the Tertiary and Cretaceous formations of Sussex* (1850) pl. 38, fig. 2.
[11] *Op. cit.*, fig. 4.

Measurements: Larger palm, holotype, length at middle, 35 millimeters; height at middle, 28 millimeters; thickness at middle, 19 millimeters; horizontal diameter of basal section of dactylus, 11 millimeters.

Occurrence: Texas: About 3 miles southwest of Farmersville, Collin County; base of Wolfe City sand, upper Taylor marl, Upper Cretaceous; 1926; A. H. Kimzey, collector; two specimens of right manus, types; also three chelae and several fragments collected in 1927, Coll. No. 13784, Cat. No. 73841.

Collection: U. S. National Museum; type, Cat. No. 73797.

Palaeastacus selmaensis Rathbun, n.sp.

(Plate 2, figure 14)

The type, a portion of a manus, is higher than in *P. kimzeyi*, but the length is undetermined; surface relatively smooth; the spines or tubercles few, four larger ones forming a curve lengthwise through the middle; lower down an irregular line of five smaller spines; besides a few other scattered tubercles the irregularities are due to punctae. Among the fragments are several indicative of a large carapace comparable to that of *P. walkeri* (Pl. 4), with well-separated tubercles or spines, but fine punctae.

Occurrence: Alabama: Wilcox County; Selma chalk; 1883; L. C. Johnson, collector: Prairie Creek and Allenton (281), one manus, holotype; Prairie Creek and Pine Barren section (284), eight fragments, chiefly of carapace, Cat. No. 73850; Prairie Creek (264), two fragments, Cat. No. 73849.

Collection: U. S. National Museum; type, Cat. No. 73848.

Family HOMARIDAE
Genus HOPLOPARIA McCoy
Hoploparia gabbi Pilsbry

(Plate 5, figures 10, 11)

1901. *Hoploparia gabbi.* Pilsbry, Philadelphia Acad. Nat. Sci., Pr., p. 115, pl. 1, figs. 11–14.
1907. *Hoploparia gabbi.* Weller, N. J. Geol. Surv., pal. ser., vol. 4, p. 846, pl. 110, figs. 12–15.
1916. *Holoparia gabbi.* Pilsbry, Md. Geol. Surv., Upper Cretaceous, p. 361, pl. 10, figs. 1–4, 8, 9.

Occurrence: New Jersey, Merchantville clay-marl; Delaware, Matawan formation; Upper Cretaceous.
Collections: Maryland Geological Survey; Philadelphia Academy of Natural Sciences, cotype, Cat. No. 527; Wagner Free Institute of Science, cotype, Cat. No. 5941.

Hoploparia gladiator Pilsbry

1901. *Hoploparia gladiator.* Pilsbry, Philadelphia Acad. Nat. Sci., Pr., p. 116, pl. 1, figs. 15 and 16.
1907. *Hoploparia gladiator.* Weller, N. J. Geol. Surv., pal. ser., vol. 4, p. 848, pl. 110, figs. 16 and 17.

1916. *Holoparia gladiator.* Pilsbry, Md. Geol. Surv., Upper Cretaceous, p. 362, pl. 10, fig. 6.

Occurrence: New Jersey, Merchantville clay-marl; Delaware, Matawan formation; Upper Cretaceous.
Collections: Wagner Free Institute of Science, type, Cat. No. 10120; Philadelphia Academy of Natural Sciences.

Hoploparia tennesseensis Rathbun

(Plate 26, figure 8)

1926. *Hoploparia tennesseensis.* Rathbun, *in* Bruce Wade, U. S. Geol. Surv., Prof. Pap. 137, p. 186, pl. 64, pl. 65, figs. 1, 3, 6.

Occurrence: Tennessee, Upper Cretaceous: Coon Creek region, McNairy County; "between Selma and Ripley formations" (probably Ripley); type-locality.
Mississippi: Lee's old mill, 2 miles northeast of Keownville on road to Molino, Union County; Ripley formation; L. W. Stephenson, collector; one specimen, part of abdomen (Cat. No. 73724).
Collections: U. S. National Museum, type, Cat. No. 73117; Vanderbilt University.

Hoploparia mcnairyensis Rathbun

1926. *Hoploparia mcnairyensis.* Rathbun, *in* Bruce Wade, U. S. Geol. Surv., Prof. Pap. 137, p. 187, pl. 65, figs. 2, 4, 5, 7, 8.

Occurrence: Tennessee: "Selma and Ripley formations" (probably Ripley), Upper Cretaceous; half a mile northwest of Gravel Hill, McNairy County (type-locality).   State Line cut, McNairy County.
Collection: U. S. National Museum; type, Cat. No. 73118.

Hoploparia georgeana Rathbun, n.sp.

(Plate 9, figures 9–12)

Proximal half or two-thirds of a large manus of a left cheliped, the distal portion partly lacking, partly fragmentary; proximal end of movable finger present.   Manus thick, width increasing rapidly from proximal end. Surface covered with low, transverse sockets irregular in size and well separated; on the more distal part of the inner surface these sockets are rounder, more swollen, and tuberculate.   On the outer surface, just above lower margin, a narrow smooth strip.   On the upper margin of the inner surface are three (at least) large, triangular, somewhat compressed spines, directed obliquely inward, almost at right angles to inner surface; between, but outside, the first and the second proximal spines, a similar erect spine on upper surface, forming a triangle; on the lower margin vestiges of four stout spines irregularly spaced.   Cross-section of dactyl oblong-oval; on the inner side of upper surface, not far from manus a large spine directed upward, inward, and distad; further back on upper half of inner surface, at articulation with manus, a smaller spine; on the prehensile edge two large lobate teeth and two small ones are visible.

Measurements: Greatest width of exposed palm, 41.7 millimeters; thickness, 27.2 millimeters.

Relation: Distinguished from *H. tennesseensis* in the more triangular outline of the palm, the row of spines on the inferior margin, and the smooth strip above that margin on the outer surface.

Occurrence: Maryland; found in an erosional exposure at Brightseat, Prince Georges County; Monmouth formation, Upper Cretaceous; R. Lee Collins, collector.

Collection: Johns Hopkins University; type.

Hoploparia dentonensis Rathbun, n.sp.

(Plate 2, figures 7-13)

Several small fragmentary palms of a species different from those described.   Palm (cotype) a little more than twice as long as wide, thick in the middle line; outer margin, slightly convex, thick, smoothly rounded; inner margin straight, with a row of three spines and a spinule (behind), and below it at proximal end a row of three small spinules. Surface covered with depressed granules.

An unattached abdomen and a carapace also from the Denton clay may belong to this species.   The abdomen is of the same bluish color as the palms.   Portions of segments 2–7 remain; the surface is abundantly punctate; the pleuron of segment 2 is broadly rounded, subcircular, with an acute point at the posterior angle.   Segments 3–5 are shorter; their pleura are truncate below, posteriorly sinuous, terminating in an acute tooth.

Carapace (182) is badly smashed; it has a brown outer layer, rough with scale-like punctae, which become sharp granules on the lateral portions; the anterior half is spinous, two rows of spines lead to the rostrum, two rows lower down on either side, a cluster of granules below the hepatic suture.

Occurrence: Texas:

Grayson County; 2 miles north of Denison, half a mile east of Kde type locality on south side St. Louis-San Francisco Railway track; Denton clay; 1920; W. S. Adkins, collector (210); five palms.

About 100 yards east of locality 210, about 2 miles north of Denison, south of St. Louis-San Francisco Railway track; Denton clay; 1920; W. S. Adkins, collector; one abdomen, one carapace.

Collection: University of Texas; cotypes, Coll. No. 210.

Hoploparia blossomana Rathbun, n.sp.

(Plate 6, figures 1-6)

A left manus lacking the extremities.   Upper and lower margins subparallel; inner surface more swollen than outer; thickness increasing toward proximal end.   Surface covered with small transverse depressions more or less reticulating and visible to naked eye; each bordered posteriorly by a slightly arcuate but flat edge; space between depressions minutely punctate. Three strong spines indicated on upper margin and, on inner surface, one near either end and a little nearer the upper than the lower margin.   Lower margin broad, smooth, somewhat flattened, and dotted with round punctae both large and small.

Measurements: Width of manus, 13 millimeters; greatest thickness, 8 millimeters.

Occurrence: Texas: About a quarter of a mile west of Detroit, Red River County; Blossom sand, Upper Cretaceous; May 20, 1907; C. H. Gordon, collector (5312); one specimen.

Collection: U. S. National Museum; type, Cat. No. 73829.

Hoploparia tarrantensis Rathbun, n.sp.
(Plate 6, figure 20)

An abdomen showing the last five segments and the right tail-fan. The terga are separated from the pleura by a smooth carina; just within, and parallel to, the carina is a shallow depression. The pleura trend well backward with arcuate sides terminating in a short acute point. The telson has on its proximal half a pair of deep, swollen sockets, followed distally by two pairs of small flat sockets; near the union with the sixth segment a pair of small swollen contiguous sockets; a lateral marginal carina and an adjacent furrow. Tail-fan longitudinally carinate; the outer branch is imperfect and shows no transverse line.

Occurrence: Texas: Blue Mound, near Haslet, Tarrant County; Denton clay, Lower Cretaceous; 1920; W. S. Adkins and W. M. and H. T. Winton, collectors.

Collection: University of Texas; type, Coll. No. 284.

Genus ISCHNODACTYLUS Pelseneer
Ischnodactylus texanus Rathbun, n.sp.
(Plate 3, figures 4–6)

Known only from the palm and the basal portion of immobile finger. Palm elongate about 1½ times as long as high; proximal and distal margins oblique and subparallel, sloping upward and backward; upper margin, slightly arcuate; lower margin sinuous—that is, arcuate under the palmar portion until near the beginning of the finger. Lower margin narrowly carinate. Prehensile margin of finger finely denticulate.

Measurements: Holotype, length of palm at middle, 9 millimeters; greatest height, 5.7 millimeters.

Occurrence: Texas; Lower Cretaceous:

Grayson County: 2½ miles north of Denison; basal 2 feet of Duck Creek limestone type-locality; one specimen, holotype; W. S. Adkins, collector (1142).

Grayson County: 2 miles north of Denison, half a mile east of Denton clay type-locality on south side St. Louis-San Francisco Railway track; 1920; numerous small specimens; W. S. Adkins, collector (210).

Northern Tarrant County: Blue Mound, 1½ miles south of Haslet station; Pawpaw clay; 1920; W. S. Adkins and W. M. Winton, collectors; one specimen; W. S. Adkins, curator (241).

Tarrant County: 4 miles southwest of Fort Worth, half a mile south of Baptist Seminary; Pawpaw; W. S. Adkins and W. M. Winton, collectors; four specimens.

Tarrant County: $4\frac{1}{2}$ miles southeast of Fort Worth, quarter of a mile south of International Great Northern Railway bridge across Sycamore Creek; Pawpaw; eight specimens; W. S. Adkins, collector (209).

Adkins reports having found the species in first hollow west of Texas Christian University, at exactly the same level as the holotype; January, 1917.

Collection: University of Texas; type, Coll. No. 1142.

Genus NEPHROPS Leach

Nephrops americanus Rathbun, n.sp.

(Plate 5, figures 6-9)

Two specimens of a right movable finger and a fragment of a left immovable one.   The dactyls as preserved are a little over twice as long as wide, depressed, end rounded but tipped with a spine (broken off).   In the larger one the prehensile edge is furnished with 17 contiguous lobes; outer edge bicarinate, the dorsal carina bearing two rows of nine sockets each, the ventral carina, or outer margin of lower surface, having six large distant spines.   Intermediate dorsal surface a deep groove with twelve granules at proximal end.   Ventral surface with a longitudinal carina subparallel to outer margin, bearing three granules on proximal half; in the depressions, proximal third punctate.

The smaller dactyl has lost its tip; its proximal end appears more nearly complete than in the larger one.   Prehensile edge with fifteen sharp lobes, not crowded, of which the middle five are largest; outer dorsal carina with two rows of seven sockets; the outer row of spines on ventral surface contains seven spines, the intermediate proximal row, four granules; on the dorsal surface the five intermediate granules are not in the depression but are nearer the inner margin and are arranged in a row.

Immovable finger shows proximal portion only, consisting chiefly of three longitudinal flutes, one outside, one above, one below, separated by deep narrow grooves; four flat-topped teeth are on prehensile edge, the basal one the largest; surface inside flutes densely punctate.

Measurements: Length of larger dactyl, 12.7 millimeters, width, 5.4 millimeters.

Relation: The dactyl in shape and ornamentation bears a curious resemblance to the palm (not finger) of *N. reedi* Carter.[12]

Occurrence: Texas; Lower Cretaceous: Tarrant County, 4 miles south-

---

[12] J. Carter: *A contribution to the palaeontology of the decapod crustacea of England*, Geol. Soc. London, Quart. Jour., vol. 54 (1898) pl. 1, fig. 1.

west of Fort Worth, half a mile south of Baptist Seminary; Pawpaw clay; W. S. Adkins and W. M. Winton, collectors.

Collection: University of Texas; cotypes, without number.

Family undetermined
Macruran undetermined

(Plate 10, figure 19)

The largest fragment showing three abdominal segments is figured for possible future identification. They are partly sculptured; the pleura are large, as long as, or longer than, broad, produced well backward, and arcuate at both ends.

Occurrence: Texas; Cretaceous: 2 miles north of Denison, Grayson County, half a mile east of Kde type-locality on south side St. Louis-San Francisco Railway track; Denton clay; 1920: W. S. Adkins, collector; four fragments of abdomen (210).

Collection: University of Texas.

Family CALLIANASSIDAE
Genus CALLIANASSA Leach
Callianassa mortoni Pilsbry

1870. *?Callianassa antiqua.* Credner, Deutsch. Geol. Ges., Zeits., vol. 22, p. 241; not *C. antiqua* Otto.

1901. *Callianassa mortoni.* Pilsbry, Philadelphia Acad. Nat. Sci., Pr., vol. 53, p. 112, pl. 1, figs. 1–7 (New Jersey and Delaware; lower marl beds).

1901. *Callianassa conradi.* Pilsbry, Philadelphia Acad. Nat. Sci., Pr., vol. 53, p. 114, pl. 1, figs. 8–10 (Crosswicks and Monmouth County, New Jersey, with *C. mortoni*).

1905. *Callianassa mortoni.* Johnson, Philadelphia Acad. Nat. Sci., Pr., vol. 57, p. 28.

1907. *Callianassa mortoni.* Weller, N. J. Geol. Surv., Paleontology, vol. 4, p. 849, pl. 111, figs. 1–15.

1907. *Callianassa conradi.* Weller, N. J. Geol. Surv., Paleontology, vol. 4, p. 851, pl. 110, figs. 18–22 (Tinton beds).

1916. *Callianassa mortoni.* Pilsbry, Md. Geol. Surv., Upper Cretaceous, p. 363, pl. 11, figs. 1–3.

1916. *Callianassa mortoni* var. *marylandica.* Pilsbry, Md. Geol. Surv., Upper Cretaceous, p. 366, pl. 11, figs. 9 and 10; type-locality, Brooks estate near Seat Pleasant, Prince Georges County, Maryland; Monmouth formation.

1916. *Callianassa clarki.* Pilsbry, Md. Geol. Surv., Upper Cretaceous, p. 368, pl. 11, figs. 6–8; type-locality, 1½ miles east of Maryland-Delaware Line on south side Chesapeake and Delaware Canal, Post 105; Matawan formation.

1926. *Callianassa mortoni.* Rathbun, *in* Bruce Wade, U. S. Geol. Surv., Prof. Pap. 137, p. 188, pl. 67, figs. 1, 2, 4–9.

In identifying chelae of *Callianassa* it must be taken into consideration that the major and the minor chela of the same specimen may differ not only in size but in form and ornamentation; that those of the female differ from those of the male and the old from the young. The wide distribution of a species also promotes diversity of form. An extensive series of specimens is needed to determine the composition of a species in this genus.   In *C. mortoni* the major and minor chelae are unlike, the minor much rougher than the major and the fingers longer and slenderer.

Occurrence: New Jersey and Delaware (type-localities); Maryland (Pilsbry), Georgia, Tennessee, Alabama, Mississippi, Arkansas, and Texas.   Upper Cretaceous.

New Jersey, F. B. Meek, 1863: First bed, green sand; G. C. Shanck, near Marlboro, Monmouth County; July 4; Cat. No. 2292.   Deep cut, Freehold and Keyport road, Monmouth County; July 4; Cat. No. 2297. First bed, green sand; North Woodward, 3 or 4 miles from New Egypt, Ocean County; July 10; Cat. No. 2427. New Jersey: Merchantville clay-marl, Navesink marl, and Tinton beds (Weller).   Woodbury clay, Lorillard; Wenonah sand, near Marlborough and near Crawford Corner; Lower Marl, Atlantic Highlands and Bruere's Pits, New Egypt; Navesink Marl, 1½ miles south of Waterford; red sand, Tinton Falls.

Delaware and Maryland: Matawan and Monmouth formations (Pilsbry).

Georgia: Chattahoochee River at Blufftown, Stewart County; Eutaw (?) formation; L. W. Stephenson, collector (5392); Cat. Nos. 73708, 73718.

Tennessee: Coon Creek region, McNairy County; "between Selma and Ripley formations" (probably Ripley) Cat. Nos. 73714, 73726.

Alabama: Eufaula, Barbour County; Ripley formation; C. B. Copeland; Cat. No. 73710.

Mississippi: Owl Creek, 3 miles northeast of Ripley, Tippah County; Ripley formation; 1889; T. W. Stanton, collector (707); four specimens (Cat. No. 73834).   Bullocks overshot mill, 2 miles southeast of Dumas, Tippah County, section 36, township 5, range 4 E.; Ripley formation; 1888; L. C. Johnson, collector (542); Cat. No. 73800.   Frisco Railroad bridge (No. 5710), 2½ miles northwest of Blue Springs, Union County; Ripley formation; June 4, 1915; L. W. Stephenson, collector (9508); Cat. No. 73788.   Houlka Creek, half a mile east of Houston, Chickasaw County; Selma chalk; T. W. Stanton, collector (612); Cat. No. 73791.

Arkansas: Upper Cretaceous: Nacatoch sand (lower part); Hot Springs road, 1.2 miles north of Arkadelphia, Clark County; April 2, 1926; L. W. Stephenson, C. H. Dane, collectors (13542); fifteen specimens (Cat. No. 73837).   Nacatoch sand; high bluff on Ouachita River, 1.5 miles above Arkadelphia (553) three specimens (Cat. No. 73836); from same locality, loose on slope, 15 to 40 feet below top of Cretaceous part of section; April 3, 1926; L. W. Stephenson and C. H. Dane, collectors (13541); three specimens (Cat. No. 73835).

Texas: Summit of small hill north of Anacacho Mt., 3 or 4 miles west of Cline, Uvalde County; Anacacho limestone; August 16, 1895; R. T. Hill and T. W. Stanton, collectors (1613b); three palms (Cat. No. 73832).

Collections: Maryland Geological Survey, Philadelphia Academy of Natural Sciences, Wagner Free Institute of Science, U. S. National Museum (types of *C. clarki* and *C. mortoni* var. *marylandica* deposited by Maryland Geological Survey); New Jersey State Museum (type of *C. conradi*).

Figured type, 1901, Wagner Free Institute of Science, Cat. No. 4059.

Callianassa mortoni var. *punctimanus* Pilsbry

1916.   *Callianassa conradi* var. *punctimanus*.   Pilsbry, Md. Geol. Surv., Upper Cretaceous, p. 368, pl. 11, figs. 6–8.

Occurrence: Delaware and Maryland; Monmouth formation.

Collection: U. S. National Museum, deposited by Maryland Geological Survey; type, without number.

Callianassa sp. indet.

1916.   *Callianassa* sp. indet.   Pilsbry, Md. Geol. Surv., Upper Cretaceous, p. 369, pl. 10, fig. 7.

Occurrence: Delaware: 1½ miles east of the Maryland-Delaware line on the south side Chesapeake and Delaware Canal; Post 105, C. & D. Canal; Matawan formation, Upper Cretaceous.

Collection: U. S. National Museum, deposited by Maryland Geological Survey.

Callianassa cretacea Rathbun, n.sp.

(Plate 6, figures 12–16)

Only the palm is known for a certainty.   Length about 1⅓ times greatest height; height diminishing from proximal to distal end.   Upper margin slightly arcuate, bordered by a narrow rim which turns the proximal corner and is rough with about 17 raised sockets, irregularly spaced; lower margin smoothly carinate, carina bowing inward and fading at the distal third, and not in line with lower margin of finger, which is farther inward. Just outside the carina a row of about eight or ten minute, distant sockets. Proximal end of palm oblique, trending forward and upward. Outer surface a little more swollen than inner; the lower carina not visible in outer view. On the lower two-fifths of the inner surface about twenty scattered, depressed granules which, however, may not represent the true outer layer of shell.

A fragmentary abdomen showing segments 3–6 may belong here.

Measurements: Middle length of palm, 11 millimeters; proximal height, 7.7 millimeters; distal height, 6.4 millimeters; thickness, 4.4 millimeters.

Occurrence: Texas; Lower Cretaceous:

Grayson County: 2 miles north of Denison, half a mile east of Denton clay type-locality on south side St. Louis-San Francisco Railway track; 1920; W. S. Adkins, collector (210); numerous, much worn specimens.

North Tarrant County: southeast of Haslet and east of Blue Mound; Denton clay; W. S. Adkins and W. M. Minton, collectors; one right palm, holotype.

Tarrant County: 4½ miles southeast of Fort Worth, quarter of a mile south of International Great Northern Railway bridge across Sycamore Creek; Pawpaw clay; one left palm; also, one abdomen, placed here with doubt; W. S. Adkins, collector (209).

Collection: University of Texas; type, Coll. No. 284.

Callianassa aquilae Rathbun, n.sp.

(Plate 7, figures 1-5)

A small specimen with a long major chela; the outer layer is badly cracked and in large part lacking. Carapace 1½ times as long as high; the gastric region, enclosed by a thumb-nail impression, is relatively short. Abdomen about 2⅗ times as long as the carapace; tail-fan carinate, outer branch with two carinae, inner with one only which has a row of seven sockets for spinules; telson wanting. Ischium and merus of major cheliped of subequal length; wrist small, less high than palm, higher than long, upper and lower margins convex. Chela elongate, narrowing distally, proximally rounded, lower margin more convex than upper, both fingers deflexed and shorter than palm, the fixed finger shorter than dactylus. The upper margin of the palm is bordered outside by eight or ten punctae; the lower margin is carinate and has 80 or more minute punctae, which are continued along the finger. This immovable finger is elongate-triangular, high at the base, gradually narrowing to an acuminate tip except for a large triangular tooth on the prehensile margin not far from the palm. Both fingers have a strong longitudinal carina; in the dactylus it is truncate and bounded either side by a deep furrow. The dactylus is slightly arched, just as high proximally as the propodal finger; the prehensile edge has a broad shallow sinus at base; a little within the margin there is a row of fine punctae disposed in pairs longitudinally. Minor chela half as wide as major, similar in form and ornamentation; a row of well-spaced punctae is visible along upper margin of dactylus.

Measurements (approximate): Holotype, length of body, 44.5 millimeters; of carapace, 12 millimeters; of major chela, 21 millimeters; of dactylus, 8 millimeters; width of palm, 7.4 millimeters.

Relation: This species approaches *Axius* in its small wrist, shape of chelae, ridged dactylus, but the short carapace and the absence of a rostrum place it in *Callianassa*.

Occurrence: Eagle Ford formation, Upper Cretaceous:

Texas: 1½ miles northeast of Sherman Junction, Grayson County, in public road ditch near base of north-facing slope of branch; May 24, 1916; L. W. Stephenson, collector (9692); one specimen, holotype.

Louisiana: Section 5, Township 13 North, Range 9 West, Red River parish, in well of Amerada Petroleum Company, Long Bell No. 1, depth 2893-2903 feet; May 31, 1927; Sidney Powers; one specimen, Cat. No. 73784.

Louisiana: Section 3, Township 11 North, Range 8 West, Natchitoches parish, in well of Amerada Petroleum Company, Wafer No. 1, depth 3165-3168 feet; May, 1927; Sidney Powers; one specimen, Cat. No. 73785.

Collection: U. S. National Museum; type, Cat. No. 73786.

Callianassa pilsbryi Rathbun, n.sp.

(Plate 7, figures 6-11)

The holotype is a right manus with fixed finger, outer surface exposed, vertically convex except along the lower border where it is flat; the upper third of the convex portion is marked off by a shallow furrow in which are five punctae in a row; the upper surface is bent over almost to the horizontal. Upper and lower margins arcuate, drawn to a thin edge closely set with outstanding tubercles which on the lower margin number about 50. Above this margin a row of 15 punctae; a similar row along the upper margin, but with longer intervals. The upper third of the surface is rough with a longitudinal band of granules irregularly placed; a line of scattered granules extends backward at the lower third of the surface, or at the level of the base of the cutting edge of the finger; and is continued upward parallel to the proximal margin, which is oblique, sloping downward and forward. Distal end vertical, bilobed, with a small triangular tooth between the lobes. Finger flat, triangular, a little longer than broad; prehensile margin double-edged, outer edge low, granulate near base of finger, four large punctae farther down; inner edge granulate or crenulate and with a tooth at middle.

A smaller left propodus is much more coarsely and thickly granulate, except in the distal two-thirds of the middle third; distal margin more oblique than in the holotype.

Two fragmentary right wrists are as long as broad, vertically convex outside, upper and lower margins thin; outer surface granulated along the distal margin, and having a distal furrow which is defined proximally by an irregular band of granules; inner surface with two clusters of granules on distal half.

Measurements: Length of right propodus (holotype) from lower proximal end of manus to tip of finger, 22 millimeters; length at middle, 15.6 millimeters; greatest width measured with dividers, 15.4 millimeters; the same distance measured over the convex surface, 19.4 millimeters; length of prehensile edge of finger, 9.5 millimeters; width of finger at base, 6 millimeters.

Occurrence: Mississippi: Frisco Railroad bridge (No. 5710) 2½ miles northwest of Blue Springs, Union County. Ripley formation; June 4, 1915; L. W. Stephenson, collector (9508).

Collection: U. S. National Museum; type, Cat. No. 73789.

Callianassa oktibbehana Rathbun, n.sp.

(Plate 6, figures 17–19)

A right, movable finger incomplete at both ends. Unusually thick for a *Callianassa*, cross-section almost as high as wide; four surfaces, upper, lower, outer, inner; outer surface straight; inner moderately concave. Upper surface a little wider than lower, with a row of 14 tubercles on outer margin; the inner, or prehensile, margin shows 12 larger tubercles. The margins bordering the lower surface are similar, but obscured. Upper surface with a row of small tubercles or granules near, and parallel to, inner edge, 16 in all, the row interrupted in four places by a hair socket; a row of five sockets near outer edge; a blunt ridge through middle of upper surface ornamented with two adjoining rows of about 18 small punctae. On the inner surface a row of three sockets just above lower margin.

Measurements: Greatest width of fragment, 4.7 millimeters; least width, 2.7 millimeters.

Occurrence: Mississippi: Gullies on campus of Agricultural and Mechanical College, Starkville, Oktibbeha County; Oktibbeha tongue of Selma chalk, November 7, 1903; A. F. Crider (3186); one specimen.

Collection: U. S. National Museum; type, Cat. No. 73825.

Callianassa valida Rathbun, n.sp.

(Plate 7, figures 12–15)

One left palm with immobile finger. Palm a little longer than broad, thick, the surfaces convex in a vertical direction except near inner base of finger; upper and lower margins parallel on distal half of palm, converging on proximal half; posterior end vertical, distal end (upper half) apparently oblique, trending backward above. Surface covered with well-separated punctae; upper margin smoothly rounded; lower margin drawn to a sharp edge armed with about ten closely appressed spinules or sockets, extending along finger also; above the margin at proximal end of inner surface, a row of six or more punctae subparallel to margin but trending toward it distally. Finger compressed, bent slightly inward, its base occupying half the height of palm, tip lacking; prehensile edge narrow, broken; on the inner side a blunt carina extends upward and a little backward on palm.

Measurements: Length of palm and finger, 9.2 millimeters; of upper margin of palm, 5.8 millimeters; middle height of palm, 4.8 millimeters.

Occurrence: Texas; Cretaceous: 2 miles north of Denison, Grayson County, half a mile east of Kde type-locality on south side St. Louis-San Francisco Railway track; Denton clay; 1920; W. S. Adkins; one specimen.

Collection: University of Texas; type, Coll. No. 210.

Callianassa bosqueana Rathbun, n.sp.

(Plate 26, figure 9)

Numerous specimens of a small elongate palm, some with the base of the immovable finger attached. Palm oval in section, with a thin upper and lower margin, rough with minute, blunt denticles. Upper margin slightly curved outward, below it a row of about 12 oblique punctae opening distad. Lower margin oblique and straight to near the base of the finger where it makes a slight turn inward; outside the margin a row of about 13 punctae. Margins of palm parallel in most cases but some specimens narrow slightly distally until just before the end. Only the base of the fixed finger is known; it is slender and bends a little downward; the cross-section is broad oval; above it, at base of finger, there is a tooth on the outer side and another opposite to it on the inner side.

Measurements: Holotype, length through middle of palm, 12.7 millimeters; greatest width, 6 millimeters. Longest palm, length 16.3 millimeters; width, 6.6 millimeters.

Occurrence: Texas; Power's Place, Valley Mills, Bosque County. Horizon, Comanche Peak formation = Fredericksburg, Cretaceous. W. S. Adkins, collector.

Collection: University of Texas, type, Coll. No. 119.

Family PALINURIDAE

Genus LINUPARUS White, 1847 = PODOCRATUS Geinitz, 1850[13]
Linuparus kleinfelderi Rathbun

(Plate 8; Plate 9, figures 1, 2; Plate 25)

1925–1926. *Holoparia gabbi.* Davis and Leng, Staten Id. Inst. Arts and Sci., Pr., vol. 4 (Oct. 1925–May 1926) p. 47, pl. 2, pl. 3 upper; not *H. gabbi* Pilsbry.

1931. *Linuparus kleinfelderi.* Rathbun, Staten Id. Inst. Arts and Sci., Pr., vol. 5, p. 131.

After the publication of the type description, a specimen was found at Great Neck, Long Island, which is more complete and shows more detail than the type material. It was referred to Percy E. Raymond, who, believing it a new species, prepared a description which is largely quoted here with his courteous permission.

"The specimen, which is in an iron-stone nodule about six inches long is a mold of the dorsal surface of the carapace and four segments of the abdomen, and a cast of the interior of the same parts. It is fortunate that the mold is preserved, for it retains evidence of the presence of many spines and tubercles which are not in any way indicated on the cast.

"Carapace elongate, narrow, the portion behind the nuchal groove strongly tri-carinate. The lateral carinae, although interrupted by the nuchal groove, extend the whole length of the carapace; the median one is confined to the posterior portion.

"The part of the carapace in front of the cervical groove is almost half (44%) of the total length. The median portion is an elevated, shield-shaped area, delimited laterally by depressions continuous with the broad concave areas between the carinae of the posterior part of the carapace. These depressions are progressively narrower toward the front, and terminate just outside the supra-orbital spines. Immediately behind these spines are short, broad-based spines which are directed forward and upward. The greater part of the shield-shaped area is covered with small tubercles; just in front of the cervical groove the tubercles are larger, outlining a roughly diamond-shaped area. At the anterior apex of the diamond is a spine somewhat larger than the others. Each of the carinae is tuberculate along the crest, at least three of the spines being larger than the others, directed upward and forward.

"The lateral portions of the carapace behind the cervical groove are turned abruptly downward. Their full extent is not shown. The entire surface behind the cervical groove is tuberculate, especially along the median and lateral carinae, each of which bears at the anterior end a prominent spine. At the posterior end of the carapace a deep furrow delimits the inflected area which overlaps the first of the free abdominal segments. This area, which is not very well preserved, appears to have supported a tall upright median spine.

"Only the tergal portions of the abdominal segments are well preserved. The first was broadly overlapped by the carapace, only about one-fourth its length being visible from the dorsal side, except near the pleural furrows, where a depressed convex triangular area is exposed. Overlap is small on the three succeeding tergites."

Each tergite has a sharp median carina. The first has a single large spine; the second tergite in the cast of the mold shows five small spines or tubercles in line; the third has seven in line on the top of its carina; the fourth has three spines or tubercles in line, followed by four staggered, these by three small ones in line.

"The pleural lappets are very badly preserved. There are indications that they were short, with spinose margins, but the outline of the single one retained is vague.

---

[13] I have followed Woods [H. Woods: *A monograph of the fossil Macrurous Crustacea of England*, Palaeontogr. Soc. London, Mem., vol. 77 (1925)] in uniting these genera.

"Measurements: Length of carapace on median line, 86 mm.; anterior margin to cervical groove, 38 mm.; greatest width of carapace 55 mm.; length of supra-occipital spines, 7 mm.; distance between tips 14 mm." Holotype; approximate length of carapace, 92 millimeters; posterior width of same, 52 millimeters.

Occurrence: New York:
Fort Wadsworth, Staten Island; Merchantville clay-marl horizon, Matawan formation, Upper Cretaceous (types).
Great Neck, Long Island; found in garden about one mile south of shore; Upper Cretaceous (Drift); Edward H. E. Wing, collector.
Collections: Staten Island Museum (types); U. S. National Museum (plastotype, Cat. No. 74474); Museum of Comparative Zoölogy, Cambridge, Mass.

Linuparus canadensis (Whiteaves)

1885. *Hoploparia ? canadensis.*   Whiteaves, Roy. Soc. Canada, Tr., 1884 (1885) vol. 2, sec. 4, p. 237–238; Canada Geol. Survey, Contr. Can. Palaeont., vol. 1, pt. 1, p. 87, pl. 11.

1895. *Podocrates canadensis.*   Whiteaves, Roy. Soc. Canada, Pr. and Tr., ser. 2, vol. 1, p. 133.

1897. *Linuparus atavus.*   Ortmann, Am. Jour. Sci., ser. 4, vol. 4, p. 293, figs. 1–4 (on p. 297).

1900. *Linuparus atavus.*   Woodward, Geol. Mag., n.s., dec. 4, vol. 7, p. 396.

1900. *Linuparus (Podocrates) canadensis.*   Woodward, Geol. Mag., n.s., dec. 4, vol. 7, p. 396, pl. 16, fig. 1.

1903. *Linuparus canadensis.*   Whiteaves, Canada Geol. Surv., Mesozoic fossils, vol. 1, pt. 5, p. 325.

1926. *Podocratus canadensis.*   Rathbun, *in* Bruce Wade, U. S. Geol. Surv., Prof. Pap. 137, p. 185, pl. 63, figs. 12, 16; U. S. Nat. Mus., Bull. 138, p. 134, pl. 35, fig. 2, pl. 36.

Occurrence: British Columbia, Alberta, South Dakota, Tennessee, Louisiana; Upper Cretaceous:
Southern Alberta: Turner Valley; Benton Shale; one large specimen (Univ. Alberta).
South Dakota: Near Whitewood, Lawrence County; Carlile formation, upper part of Benton group; from Mrs. Charles J. Haas; Cat. No. 73712.
Tennessee: Half a mile northwest of Gravel Hill, McNairy County; "between Selma and Ripley formations," probably Ripley; Cat. No. 73116.
Louisiana: Natchitoches Parish, Section 3, Township 11 North, Range 8 West, well of Amerada Petroleum Company, Wafer No. 1; in core sample taken at a depth of 3165 feet to 3168 feet and furnished by Sidney Powers, May 1927; showing midrib of hind part of carapace; Eagle Ford formation; Cat. No. 73798.
Collections: U. S. National Museum, cast of type, Cat. No. 73717; University of Alberta, type.

Linuparus vancouverensis (Whiteaves)

(Plate 10, figures 1–3)

1895. *Podocrates vancouverensis.*   Whiteaves, Roy. Soc. Canada, Tr., vol. 1, sec. 4, p. 132.

1900. *Linuparus (Podocrates) vancouverensis.*   Woodward, Geol. Mag., n.s., dec. 4, vol. 7, p. 393, pl. 15, figs. 1–3.

1903. *Linuparus vancouverensis.*   Whiteaves, Geol. Surv. Canada, Mesozoic fossils, vol. 1, pt. 5, p. 323, pl. 40, figs. 1–3.

1926. *Podocratus vancouverensis.*   Rathbun, U. S. Nat. Mus., Bull. 138, p. 135, pl. 37.

Occurrence:
Oklahoma: Bryan County: Bluff on Washita River at Frisco R. R. bridge, left bank, 2½ miles east of Platter; Marietta formation of Denison group of Comanche series; August 12, 1917; L. W. Stephenson (602); two specimens, Cat. No. 73706.
British Columbia: Type-localities: 2 miles up Puntledge River, Vancouver Island; also Hornby Island; Nanaimo group.
Collections: U. S. National Museum; Geological Survey of Canada, Museum, Ottawa, types.

Linuparus adkinsi Rathbun, n.sp.

(Plate 10, figures 4–10)

1918. *Hoploparia ?*. Adkins, Univ. Texas, Bull. 1856, p. 62.
1928. *Thenops* n.sp. aff. *tuberculatus*. Adkins, Univ. Texas, Bull. 2838, p. 83.

A small species, the body not exceeding 32 millimeters in length. Dorsal surface of carapace moderately arched transversely, covered with fine-spaced granules. Anterior margin produced forward at the outer angles in a stout spine. Another spine at inner angle of each orbit; the distance between them one-quarter of anterior width of carapace. A short median carina, its anterior half lower and composed of smaller granules than the posterior half; behind the carina an oblong flat area, open at the ends and with a slightly arcuate carina on either side. Behind the inner orbital spines, and farther forward than the median carina, a stout spine followed by a short carina, which gradually diminishes to the level of the carapace. Beginning at the same anterior line, a long carina reaching to the cervical groove; it is nearly longitudinal but is curved slightly outward, its hinder end farther from the median line than the anterior end; armed with an anterior spine and one a little in front of the middle. Outside this carina the surface descends steeply to a linear impressed groove parallel to the carina; thence it becomes almost horizontal. Cervical grooves deep and broad, at less than a right angle to each other and meeting in a transverse groove at the middle. Behind the grooves are three nearly parallel, longitudinal granulated carinae, the median one with a double row of granules. Exterior to the lateral carina the carapace slopes nearly vertically downward except near the cervical groove, where the upper part is concave and the lower convex. In front of the posterior margin of the carapace, a broad smooth groove behind the median carina and curving backward on each side becomes narrower toward the lateral margin.

Abdomen about same length as carapace. The terga have a linear median carina without spines and consisting of a single line of granules and are otherwise covered with flat granules except along the posterior and the anterior margins and on an oblique depression near the lateral extremities. The pleura follow the bend of the terga; pleuron of second somite longer, in the axial direction of the animal, than wide, and with a postlateral angle almost a right angle; pleura of third, fourth, and fifth somites wider than long, margins arcuate, extremities subacute. Last two somites unknown.

Measurements: Carapace (284), length, 15.7 millimeters; width, 8.3 millimeters. Abdomen (182), length of first five somites, 11.5 millimeters; width at second somite, 8.4 millimeters.

Relation: Closely allied to *L. carteri* (Reed)[14] of the Lower Greensand of England, but differs in its smaller size, the absence of a median carina from anterior half of carapace, and the presence of an antero-lateral spine.

Occurrence: Texas; Denton clay; W. S. Adkins:
Grayson County, two miles north of Denison and half a mile east of type-locality of Denton clay, on south side of St. Louis-San Francisco Railway track; loc. 210; 1920; thirty specimens.
About 100 yards east of loc. 210, about two miles north of Denison, south of St. Louis-San Francisco Railway track; loc. 182; eight specimens.
Northern Tarrant County, southeast of Haslet and east of Blue Mound; W. S. Adkins and W. M. Winton, collectors; two specimens (one is holotype).
Collection: University of Texas; type, Coll. No. 284.

---

[14] *Thenops carteri*. F. R. C. Reed: *New crustacea from the lower Greensand of the Isle of Wight*, Geol. Mag., n.s., dec. 5, vol. 8 (1911) p. 116, pl. 7, fig. 2. *T. tuberculatus. Op. cit.*, p. 118, pl. 7, fig. 1. *Linuparus carteri*. H. Woods: *A monograph of the fossil macrurous crustacea of England*, Pal. Soc. London, Mem., vol. 77, 1923 (1925) p. 78 [28], pl. 7, figs. 2 and 3.

Linuparus (?) sp.

(Plate 9, figure 6)

A fragment from perhaps the hinder part of carapace. Surface tuberculate.

Occurrence: Mississippi: Frisco Railroad bridge (No. 5710), 2½ miles northwest of Blue Springs, Union County; Ripley formation, June 4, 1915; L. W. Stephenson; one specimen.

Collection: U. S. National Museum, Cat. No. 73843.

Linuparus (?) sp.

(Plate 16, figure 15)

A fragment from hinder part of carapace, covered with pointed granules depressed in pits, the points directed forward.

Occurrence: Texas: Tarrant County, 4¼ miles southeast of Fort Worth, quarter of a mile south of International Great Northern Railway bridge across Sycamore Creek; Pawpaw clay; W. S. Adkins; one fragment (209).

Collection: University of Texas.

Genus ARCHAEOCARABUS McCoy
Archaeocarabus (?) *whitfieldi* (Pilsbry)

(Plate 10, figures 11, 12)

1901. *Cancer* (?) *whitfieldi.* Pilsbry, Philadelphia Acad. Nat. Sci., Pr., vol. 53, p. 118, pl. 1, fig. 18.

Apparently the right palm of a large specimen, but crushed and narrowed laterally. It is thickest in the upper part, and the upper surface is well defined; this is furnished with three longitudinal rows of stout conical spines, one on each margin and one through the middle; the outer row consists of six spines, the two distal small, the row curving downward at middle, the spines outstanding; the inner row also curved downward consists of six larger spines, the proximal one the largest, all outstanding; five, or perhaps six, erect spines in the shorter median row. On the flat outer surface a row of four rather small spines a little above the middle and subparallel to the marginal row. At the proximal end near the top two small spines. On the lower distal quarter two isolated spines. Lower surface about half as wide as upper, rounding from one side to the other and showing, though much broken, traces of two rows of spines; two spines remain of the outer row and two of the inner. Much of the inner surface is lacking; there is a triangle of three small spines at the upper proximal end, and a single spine near the lower distal corner. General surface smooth or nearly so.

The fingers are absent, but their position is shown in figure 12. The propodal finger is short and projects directly distad. The dactylus is attached below the top of the manus and folds transversely against the distal end of it.

Measurements: Holotype, right (?) manus, length, 36.2 millimeters; width near the middle, 27 millimeters.

Occurrence: New Jersey: Burlington County; Upper Cretaceous; S. Wetherill, collector; one specimen, holotype.

Collection: Philadelphia Academy of Natural Sciences, type, Cat. No. 4693.

Family PAGURIDAE
Genus PAGURISTES Dana
Paguristes ouachitensis Rathbun, n.sp.
(Plate 6, figures 9–11)

Distal portion of a left palm with stump of dactylus attached. Palm below thick; above narrow with blunt margin; palm lower at distal end than farther back. Inner surface nearly flat, forming an obtuse angle with the lower surface; outer surface swollen in the lower distal portion. Cross-sections of fingers subequal. Surface of palm and finger base covered with unequal scaly granules, some of which are double; those on upper edge are larger and more outstanding.

Measurements: Greatest height of palm, 10 millimeters; height at distal end, 9 millimeters; greatest thickness, 5.4 millimeters.

Occurrence: Arkansas: High bluff on Ouachita River, 1.5 miles above Arkadelphia, Clark County; from lower masses at base of bluff; Nacatoch sand; April 3, 1926; L. W. Stephenson and C. H. Dane, collectors (Coll. No. 13543); one specimen.

Collection: U. S. National Museum, type, Cat. No. 73828.

Genus PAGURUS Fabricius
Pagurus banderensis Rathbun, n.sp.
(Plate 9, figures 7, 8)

The distal portion of a right chela showing fingers and adjacent palm. Surface for the most part covered with large pointed granules not contiguous and directed obliquely distad; on the inner surface the longitudinal furrow on immovable finger is smooth, also that part of palm not bordering the fingers. Lower margin of specimen concave except near tip of finger where it is slightly ascending. Fingers gaping at base. Immobile finger half as high at base as it is long and of uniform height to its middle; outer surface as well as inner with a shallow longitudinal furrow; prehensile edge with about eight lobiform teeth, the largest one at the bend in the outline; tip blunt. Dactylus closed within fixed finger, equally high at base gradually diminishing, upper line arcuate, outer surface with a narrow furrow on which granules are scanty, prehensile edge concave and furnished with small tubercles; tip lacking, but did not reach end of fixed finger. Palm vertical at base of dactyl, swollen outwardly along the gape and the fixed finger as far as the bend; upper margin lacking.

Measurements: Height of palm near fingers, 19.6 millimeters; length of fixed finger along prehensile margin, 15 millimeters; length of dactylus on upper margin, 19.5 millimeters.

Occurrence: Texas: One mile east of Bandera, Bandera County; Glen Rose formation, *Salenia texana* horizon; one specimen.

Collection: University of Texas, type.

Genus PETROCHIRUS Stimpson
Petrochirus taylori Rathbun, n.sp.

(Plate 3, figures 1-3)

The distal portion of a left fixed finger, the surface much worn and the extreme tip broken off. The surface exposed when the fingers are closed is covered with low circular elevations, unequal and separated, which have, for the most part, a hollow center but in some cases retain suggestion of a cluster of granules. Prehensile surface smoothly hollowed; cutting edge on outer side lacking but represented by a row of fine parallel lines; margin of inner side with a row of depressions which were doubtless occupied by as many tubercles.

Occurrence: Texas: Reported to have come from upper part of Taylor marl, Gulf series, at base of Wolfe City sand; 3 miles southwest of Farmersville, Collin County; 1927; A. H. Kimzey, collector (13784); one specimen.

Collection: U. S. National Museum, type, Cat. No. 73826.

Family DAKOTICANCRIDAE
Genus DAKOTICANCER Rathbun
Dakoticancer overana Rathbun

1917. *Dakoticancer overana.* Rathbun, U. S. Nat. Mus., Pr., vol. 52, p. 386, pl. 32, pl. 33, figs. 6–14.

1926. *Dakoticancer overana.* Rathbun, *in* Bruce Wade, U. S. Geol. Surv., Prof. Pap. 137, p. 189, pl. 67, fig. 3.

Occurrence:

South Dakota; Pierre shale, Upper Cretaceous: West side, Missouri River, a short distance below Mobridge, eastern Corson County (type-locality). Also Indian Creek, Pennington County.

New Jersey; Cliffwood Clay; Cliffwood; the imprint of the dorsal surface of a carapace 19 millimeters long.

Tennessee, "Selma-Ripley formations," (probably Ripley), Upper Cretaceous: McNairy County: Half a mile northwest of Gravel Hill; State Line cut on Southern Railway, 1 mile northwest of Wenasoga, Miss.; also a few hundred yards west of Wenasoga station.

Collections: U. S. National Museum, type, Cat. No. 32055; University of South Dakota; New Jersey State Museum.

Dakoticancer overana australis Rathbun, n. subsp.

(Plate 10, figure 20)

This form differs from the typical one in the greater extent of the granulation of the carapace, the smooth areas restricted to narrow depressions between the elevations instead of covering their slopes as in the typical form. The carapace is narrower, although exact figures are not available, as no specimen is provided with a complete rostrum. The single rostrum is compressed at base and widens slightly toward the extremity. A female paratype (73840) measures 35.1 millimeters long from the orbital margin and 40 millimeters wide, or 1:1.14, whereas a typical *overana* (32056) measures 19.4:24.7 or 1:1.27.

Occurrence: Upper Cretaceous:

Mississippi: Ripley formation: Whitten farm in the southwest corner of the southwest quarter of Section 21, Township 8 South, Range 4 East, Union County; June 21, 1925; presented by N. C. Whitten, obtained by L. W. Stephenson, collector (11648); six large specimens (one is holotype).

Texas: Navarro formation (chalky marl member); cut in San Antonio road, 6 miles east of Castroville, Bexar County; April 8, 1932; L. W. Stephenson, collector (16156); half of a carapace, Cat. No. 74585.

Collection: U. S. National Museum, type, Cat. No. 73840.

Genus TETRACARCINUS Weller
Tetracarcinus subquadratus Weller

(Plate 10, figures 16–18)

1905. *Tetracarcinus subquadratus.* Weller, Jour. Geol., vol. 13, p. 328, figs. 4–6;
     N. J. State Geol., Ann. Rept. for 1904 (1905) p. 136, 139, 141, pl. 15, figs. 4–6.
1907. *Tetracarcinus subquadratus.* Weller, N. J. Geol. Surv., Paleont. ser., vol. 4,
     p. 852, atlas, pl. 111, figs. 16–19.

Occurrence:
New Jersey, Upper Cretaceous: Cliffwood clay, Cliffwood Point and near Matawan (type-localities); Woodbury clay, Lorillard (13 specimens). (Weller.) Cliffwood clay, Cliffwood Brick Company, ventral and palm; Tinton beds, Beers Hills, sternum and palm.

Wyoming: Lewis shale, Upper Cretaceous; 8 miles west of Rawlins, on Lincoln Highway (loc. 10722); one specimen, Cat. No. 73716.

Collections: New Jersey State Museum, types; U. S. National Museum. The carapace reaches a length of 19 millimeters.

Family DYNOMENIDAE
Genus GRAPTOCARCINUS Roemer
Graptocarcinus texanus Roemer

(Plate 10, figures 13–15)

1887. *Graptocarcinus texanus.* Roemer, Neues Jahrb. f. Min., Geol., Palaeont., vol.
     1, p. 173, text-fig.
1913. *Graptocarcinus texanus.* Whitney, Texas Acad. Sci., Tr., vol. 12, p. 27, pl. 13,
     figs. 1 and 2.

To the measurements already given (cotype, length, 28 millimeters; width, 36 millimeters) may be added the fronto-orbital width, 14.3 millimeters or two-fifths the carapace width. The granules of the outer layer of shell are lower and less prominent than on the inner layer. The slight notch in the antero-lateral margin marks the terminus of the subbranchial suture. The median furrow on the frontal region is broad and smooth.

Occurrence: Texas:
Shoal Creek, at 29th Street (type-locality), and Barton Creek (Whitney), Austin, Travis County; lower part of Buda limestone. Two cotypes (Univ. Texas), one specimen, Cat. No. 73851.

In the bank of a dry river near Austin; probably Buda limestone; Eleanor J. Pond; one specimen, Cat. No. 31096.

Collections: University of Texas, U. S. National Museum.

Genus XANTHOSIA Bell
Xanthosia aspera Rathbun, n.sp.

(Plate 11, figures 1–5)

Two specimens from the type locality, the more complete one badly broken; carapace nearly twice as wide as long. Surface uneven, divided into large nodules separated by deep grooves and rough with conical tubercles of unequal size and unevenly disposed. Four median tubercles, the two gastric smaller than the two cardiac. A protogastric nodule, two nodules following the antero-lateral margin and one at the inner branchial angle. A broad furrow runs from the mesogastric region obliquely backward to the antero-lateral margin between the second and the third lobes, another furrow to the postero-lateral margin. Antero-lateral margin thin, obscurely four-lobed. Fronto-orbital width half of carapace width; front broken off; a narrow, nearly vertical, black band near the inner end of the orbit. Postero-lateral margin thick, concave. Pterygostomian region minutely granulate, with larger granules of varying size interspersed. Abdomen of female with two longitudinal furrows; first two somites dorsal in position. Color bluish.

A fragment of a larger specimen was taken at a nearby station. It is one-quarter larger than the holotype.

Measurements: Female, holotype, length of carapace, rostrum excluded, 7.7 millimeters; width of same, 14 millimeters or upwards.

Occurrence: Texas: Grayson County; Denton clay:

Two miles north of Denison, half a mile east of Kde type-locality on south side St. Louis-San Francisco Railway track; 1920; W. S. Adkins, collector; one fragment (210).

About 100 yards east of locality 210, about 2 miles north of Denison, south of St. Louis-San Francisco Railway track; 1920; W. S. Adkins, collector; holotype and paratype (182).

Collection: University of Texas, types, Coll. No. 182.

Xanthosia wintoni Rathbun, n.sp.

(Plate 11, figures 6-8)

Carapace less than twice as wide as long, fronto-orbital width two-thirds of carapace width. Antero-lateral edge thin, cut into five shallow teeth of which the fifth is a little thicker and forms the lateral angle of the carapace. Surface covered with large granules, not continuous; the tops are mostly broken off, giving the appearance of punctae. Furrows shallow; on the branchial region a transverse furrow in line with the widest part of the mesogastric region. Where the outer layer, or layers, of shell are lacking, the carapace shows more distinctly the furrows characteristic of the genus: The two transverse or subtransverse furrows and those surrounding the gastric and the cardiac regions; also in evidence are two groups of three punctae or sockets, forming a triangle on the cardiac and on the urogastric region.

Measurements: No. 210, width of carapace, 11 millimeters; fronto-orbital width, 7.4 millimeters; hind part of carapace absent.

Occurrence: Texas; Cretaceous:

Grayson County, 2 miles north of Denison, half a mile east of Kde type-locality on south side St. Louis-San Francisco Railway track; Denton clay; 1920; one specimen, holotype; W. S. Adkins, collector.

Grayson County, about 100 yards east of locality 210, about 2 miles north of Denison, south of St. Louis-San Francisco track; Denton clay; 1920; two specimens; W. S. Adkins, collector (182).

Northern Tarrant County at Blue Mound, 1½ miles south of Haslet station; Pawpaw; 1920; two specimens; W. S. Adkins and W. M. Winton, collectors (241).

Collection: University of Texas, type, Coll. No. 210.

Family DROMIIDAE
Genus DROMIA Fabricius
Dromia (?) *anomala* Rathbun, n.sp.

(Plate 11, figures 10, 11)

A small carapace with a manus underneath is placed here tentatively. It is broad-oval, convex from side to side; rostrum lacking; surface smooth (non-granulate); a narrow median carina extends from the anterior margin to less than one-third the carapace-length; either side a short oblique carina trends forward and inward to the margin; a short cervical groove forms a broad V at about the posterior third of the median line; near the posterior end of the carapace there is a broad shallow, median elevation; lateral margin unknown.

The accompanying manus is stout, inner surface flattened, outer convex and covered with small, crisp, well-separated granules; if it is a right manus, the fragmentary attachment at the extreme left (fig. 11) represents the carpus.

Occurrence: Texas: Grayson County; 2 miles north of Denison, half a mile east of the Kde type-locality on south side St. Louis-San Francisco Railway track; Denton clay; 1920; W. S. Adkins, collector.

Collection: University of Texas, type, Coll. No. 210.

Family CALAPPIDAE
Genus NECROCARCINUS Bell

Key to the American species of *Necrocarcinus*.

A¹. A transverse row of five conical, blunt spines on the gastric region, the one on the median line being the anterior one of a longitudinal row of five...*pierrensis*

A². A transverse row of four conical spines on the gastric region.

    B¹. Several median spines.

        C¹. Eight median spines and as many spines on a longitudinal branchial ridge...........................*oklahomensis*

C². Three or four median spines.

D¹. Two large well-separated median spines on gastric region.

texensis

D². Two small adjacent median spines at hinder end of gastric region. One spine at least on cardiac region.

graysonensis

B². Less than three median spines.

C¹. Two median spines..............................*hannae*[15]

C². One large median spine...............*Necrocarcinus* (?) sp.

Necrocarcinus oklahomensis Rathbun, n.sp.

(Plate 11, figure 9)

Carapace of holotype subcircular, wider in anterior half, not counting spines. Three longitudinal carinae, the median beginning half way along the gastric region, interrupted at the cervical suture and extending nearly to posterior margin; rough with small tubercles, four in front of the suture, three behind. Lateral carinae extending the length of the branchial region, diverging a little posteriorly, and having eight unequal tubercles, the posterior one just above postero-lateral angle of carapace. Across the epibranchial region a short carina armed with two tubercles and inclined obliquely backward to the margin, where it terminates in what appears to be the largest marginal spine. A transverse row of two tubercles on each protogastric region; an hepatic tubercle in same line. Of marginal spines there are four antero-lateral between orbit and hepatic sinus, two immediately behind the sinus; three unequal post-lateral tubercles; one on either side of posterior margin forming an obtuse angle with the posterior median spine. Front and orbits displaced. Length of carapace, about 30.6 millimeters; width without spines, 36 millimeters.

A paratype of small size shows the anterior three-quarters and right three-fifths of carapace. Fronto-orbital distance half of width of carapace. Margins of front elevated. Surface minutely and closely granulate. Furrows deep either side of gastro-cardiac region; narrow grooves define the anterior end of mesogastric region. Blunt pyramidal tubercles as follows: two in transverse line on each protogastric region, the inner much larger than outer. One large hepatic tubercle behind the line of the protogastric tubercles. The surface in front of these six tubercles is concave. The tubercles of the longitudinal carinae are fewer than in the mature specimen; three median tubercles of which two small are near together on the posterior gastric, one large on cardiac region. Two branchial tubercles on the carina. In side view the lateral margin is sinuous, its spines or blunt tubercles

---

[15] M. J. Rathbun: *The fossil stalk-eyed crustacea of the Pacific slope of North America*, U. S. Nat. Mus., Bull. 138 (1926) p. 84, pl. 18, figs. 1 and 2.

directed obliquely upward. Counting from the orbit there are five small (one of which is behind the sinus), two large, one small; the large ones are elevated and form a right-angle triangle with the outermost of the dorsal spines. Width of carapace, about 18 millimeters.

Occurrence: Oklahoma: Bryan County: Bluff on Washita River at Frisco Railroad bridge, left bank, 2½ miles east of Platter; Marietta formation of Denison group of Comanche series; August 12, 1917; L. W. Stephenson, collector (602); one specimen, holotype.

Collection: U. S. National Museum, type, Cat. No. 73713.

Necrocarcinus pierrensis (Rathbun)

(Plate 12, figure 5)

1917. *Campylostoma pierrense.* Rathbun, U. S. Nat. Mus., Pr., vol. 52, p. 389, pl. 33, figs. 4 and 5.

Occurrence: South Dakota: Eastern Corson County; Pierre shale, Upper Cretaceous; W. H. Over, collector; two specimens including holotype (Cat. No. 32057).
New Jersey: Lorillard; Woodbury clay; an incomplete carapace.
The New Jersey specimen is without a marginal line, but its 13 spines are arranged as in the type specimens.
Collections: U. S. National Museum, types, Cat. No. 32057; New Jersey State Museum.

Necrocarcinus graysonensis Rathbun, n.sp.

(Plate 11, figures 23–25)

Represented by a single specimen, the right, anterior portion of a carapace. Antero-lateral margin slightly arcuate, bearing a row of five small equidistant spines beginning near the orbit and followed by two larger ones on a higher level and then another small spine lower down. On the gastric region two small adjacent median spines near the posterior end, and a transverse row of four spines, the middle pair larger than the outer pair, the median interspace greater than the lateral; farther forward and outward, a spine behind the orbit; one hepatic spine, one cardiac, four branchial, forming a rhomboid.

Width of carapace, 17.3 millimeters; length from orbit (tip broken) to gastro-cardiac suture, 9 millimeters.

Occurrence: Texas: Grayson County: 2 miles north of Denison, half a mile east of Kde type-locality on south side St. Louis-San Francisco Railway track; Denton clay; 1920; one specimen, holotype; W. S. Adkins, collector.

Collection: University of Texas, type, Coll. No. 210.

Necrocarcinus texensis Rathbun, n.sp.

(Plate 11, figures 20–22)

Carapace convex longitudinally and transversely; surface microscopically punctate; three blunt longitudinal carinae and thirteen large tubercles; the median carina begins about half way between the front and the gastro-cardiac furrow, diminishes in height toward the posterior margin and is armed with three round tubercles, the anterior the largest, the posterior or cardiac the next in size; a granule on the posterior slope of the middle tubercle, and also one behind the cardiac tubercle. The branchial carina begins on the line of the branchio-cardiac suture, and narrows to the posterior margin; it has an elongate longitudinal tubercle at its anterior end, the largest tubercle on the carapace, and a small low tubercle near the posterior end. Two tubercles on the epibranchial slope almost transverse in position, the outer slightly in advance, the inner directly in front of the branchial carina. Two smaller tubercles placed transversely on the protogastric region, on a line in advance of the median carina, the inner tubercle smaller but more elevated than the outer. The right margin shows the bases of three stout teeth and a small denticle farther forward, near the outer margin of the orbit.

A larger specimen, about 17 millimeters wide, is more incomplete and more worn but corresponds in general features to the type.

Measurements (approximate): Holotype, length of carapace measured from base of front, 9 millimeters; width of carapace, 11.9 millimeters; width between outer angles of orbits, 4.6 millimeters; width between posterior angles of carapace, 6 millimeters.

Relation: The species resembles *N. tricarinatus* Bell[16] in its carinae, but the furrow between meso- and metabranchial lobes is less deep, the sculpturing less marked. The front more nearly resembles that of *N. woodwardii*,[17] the fronto-orbital width being only a third of carapace-width.

Occurrence: Texas:

Grayson County, about 100 yards east of locality 210, about 2 miles north of Denison, south of St. Louis-San Francisco track; Denton clay; 1920; one carapace, holotype; W. S. Adkins, collector.

Northern Tarrant County, Haslet station at Blue Mound; Pawpaw; 1920; W. S. Adkins and W. M. Winton, collectors (241); one carapace.

Collection: University of Texas, type, Coll. No. 182.

Necrocarcinus (?), sp.

(Plate 11, figure 31; Plate 13, figure 6)

An oval fragment of carapace, showing thirteen large tubercles arranged in three rows of four, five, four, the tubercles alternating, is impossible to place with certainty; the outer edge shows traces of four marginal tubercles (Pl. 11, fig. 31). A second piece with smaller and more numerous worn tubercles irregularly placed may also belong here (Pl. 13, fig. 6).

Occurrence: Texas: Tarrant County, 4½ miles southeast of Fort Worth,

---

[16] T. Bell: *A monograph of the fossil malacostracous crustacea of Great Britain*, pt. 2, Palaeont. Soc., London 1862 (1863) p. 21, pl. 4, figs. 9–11.

[17] *Op. cit.*, p. 20, pl. 4, figs. 1–3.

quarter of a mile south of International Great Northern Railway bridge across Sycamore Creek; Pawpaw clay; W. S. Adkins, collector (209).

Collection: University of Texas.

Genus PREHEPATUS, n.gen.

The chelae differ from the rest of the Calappidae in the palmar portion bent horizontally to form an upper surface. In *Hepatus* there is a tendency in that direction.

Genotype: *P. cretaceus* Rathbun, n.sp.

Prehepatus cretaceus Rathbun, n.sp.

(Plate 11, figures 29, 30)

Holotype, a right chela. Palm increasing in height gradually to the distal end, superior length a little greater than distal height. Surface, convex transversely, gradually rounding into a broad upper surface, whose free margin is quinquedentate and depressed so as not to be visible from outer side. The most protuberant part of the outer surface has two longitudinal rows of four large conical tubercles; below are six smaller tubercles irregularly placed; on the upper surface are ten tubercles, also small. The upper surface is widest at posterior end, which is oblique, the free portion arcuate and carinate, the marginal teeth also carinate, the distal tooth overlapping the dactylus a little. Lower margin of palm armed at distal end with three small conical tubercles pointing downward, followed by a few minute denticles on the finger. Remainder of lower margin of propodus lacking. Distal end of outer surface of palm oblique, the dactylus being much longer on upper margin than propodal finger (tip broken off). Fingers meeting when closed. Fixed finger with a longitudinal furrow on outer surface; the prehensile edge bears a long low tooth flanked at either end by a small tooth. Dactylus thick and high, a prehensile tooth fits in the cavity proximal to the teeth of the opposing finger; three lobes at base of upper margin; on upper surface a small tubercle opposite proximal lobe; blunt outer carina granulate at base; tip of finger thick and blunt.

Measurements: Length of chela, 13 millimeters; distal height of palm, 8 millimeters; proximal height of palm, 5.5 millimeters; greatest width of upper surface, 4.6 millimeters.

Relation: The dactylus, *"Pseudomicippe" granulosa* Pelseneer[18] may belong to the same genus as the species above described.

Occurrence: Texas: Grayson County, 3 miles north of Denison, on south bank of Duck Creek, in marl above *Pervinquieria aff. trinodosa;* type locality of Duck Creek limestone; one right, major chela, holotype; W. S. Adkins, collector.

Collection: University of Texas, type, Coll. No. 211.

[18] P. Pelseneer: *Notice sur les crustacés décapodes du Maestrichtien du Limbourg,* Mus. Roy. Hist. Nat. Belgique, Bull., vol. 4 (1886) p. 170 [10], fig. 6.

Prehepatus pawpawensis Rathbun, n.sp.

(Plate 11, figures 26–28)

Holotype, a small left chela, lacking the fixed finger and tip of dactylus. Small tubercles mixed with granules much more numerous than in *P. cretaceus*, especially on upper surface and lower part of outer surface; proximal margin more oblique and lower margin more arcuate, the latter armed with about fifteen minute sharp granules. A curved row of granules on inner surface. Numerous granules on upper base of finger; three superior lobes faintly indicated, as are also four teeth on the inner margin of propodus, the distal tooth broken off.

Measurements: Length of palm, 6 millimeters; distal height, 4.3 millimeters; proximal height measured on oblique margin, 3.5 millimeters; greatest width of upper surface, 2 millimeters.

Occurrence: Tarrant County, 4 miles southwest of Fort Worth, half a mile south of Baptist Seminary; Pawpaw; W. S. Adkins and W. M. Winton, collectors; one left, minor chela, holotype.

Collection: University of Texas, type, without number.

Family RANINIDAE
Genus NOTOPOCORYSTES McCoy
Notopocorystes punctatus Rathbun, n.sp.

(Plate 12, figures 14–16)

A small carapace, lacking the frontal margin and the hinder end. Carapace thick and high, covered with closely placed punctae outside and with granules on an inferior layer. The lateral surface is without a marginal line and is smoothly rounded downward except for a short antero-lateral tooth (tip broken off), at a distance from the orbit equal to about one-third the fronto-orbital distance. Two notches in upper margin of right orbit indicate a front akin to that of *N. parvus*. Subhepatic region not furrowed.

Measurements: Greatest width of carapace, 6.7 millimeters; fronto-orbital width, 5.5 millimeters; width between first and second pereiopods, 4.8 millimeters; distance from antero-lateral tooth to base of outer orbital tooth, 1.6 millimeters.

Occurrence: Texas: Grayson County, 2 miles north of Denison, half a mile east of Kde type-locality on south side St. Louis-San Francisco Railway track; Denton clay, Cretaceous; 1920; W. S. Adkins, collector.

Collection: University of Texas, type, Coll. No. 210.

Notopocorystes parvus Rathbun, n.sp.

(Plate 12, figures 11–13)

A small, incomplete specimen of carapace showing the anterior end, the right margin of the dorsum, and the ventral surface; hinder end lacking.

A small blunt marginal tooth at widest part of carapace; in front of it a larger triangular tooth with a long posterior margin. Orbital lobes subtruncate, separated by narrow sinuses; outer orbital angle slightly produced; next lobe slightly arcuate. Rostrum broken off; a short median carina at base. Lower surface of carapace finely granulate; a deep triangular furrow behind the orbit, the point of the triangle extending to the level of the anterior lateral tooth.

Measurements: Greatest width of carapace, 7 millimeters; width at orbits, 5.6 millimeters.

Relation: The front resembles that of *N. carteri* McCoy,[19] which, however, has three instead of two lateral teeth.

Occurrence: Texas: Tarrant County at Blue Mound, near Haslet; Denton clay, Cretaceous; 1920; W. S. Adkins and W. M. and Hortense T. Winton, collectors.

Collection: University of Texas, type, Coll. No. 284.

Notopocorystes (?) *ripleyensis* Rathbun, n.sp.

(Plate 12, figures 6–10)

A right manus lacking the lower distal end and with a stump of the dactylus attached. Manus thick, about three-quarters as wide as its greatest length, upper and lower margins slightly arcuate; outer surface gradually rounding into the upper surface which is broad; two rows of stout, conical spines above, well over on the inner half, the outer row with six spines, the inner with four; the outer row is slightly curved inward, the inner row is shorter and more strongly curved. Three blunt carinae on the outer-upper surface, the upper carina near to, and paralleling, the row of spines and separated from it by a deep furrow; of the straight outer carinae the lower one is at the middle, the other gradually diverges from it distally and is nearer the upper carina. Lower surface thick, subtruncate, narrowing steadily to the distal end, which is half as wide as the proximal end. The inner surface has a twisted appearance; below the overhanging quadrispinose row, described above, there is a broad furrow which is deepest at the proximal end. Above the lower margin there is a narrower furrow which tapers from the distal end backward to a point before reaching the proximal end. The base of the dactylus shows a spine in line with the outer row on the manus; a furrow on the inner surface corresponds to that on the manus, and another furrow, just outside the spine, also is in line with the outer propodal furrow.

Measurements: Proximal width of manus, 5 millimeters; distal width, 8.2 millimeters; thickness at the middle, 4.2 millimeters.

Occurrence: Mississippi: Tupelo road, 1 mile east of Pontotoc, Pontotoc

---

[19] F. McCoy: *On some new Cretaceous crustacea*, Ann. Mag. Nat. Hist., ser. 2, vol. 14 (1854) p. 118, pl. 4, fig. 3.

County; Ripley formation; L. W. Stephenson, collector (Coll. No. 6855); holotype.

Collection: U. S. National Museum, type, Cat. No. 73792.

Genus RANINELLA A. Milne Edwards
Raninella testacea Rathbun

1926. *Raninella testacea.*   Rathbun, *in* Bruce Wade, U. S. Geol. Surv., Prof. Pap. 137, p. 190, pl. 68.

Occurrence: Tennessee; Ripley formation; Coon Creek, McNairy County (type-locality).
Collection: U. S. National Museum, type, Cat. No. 73121.

Raninella mucronata[20] Rathbun, n.sp.
(Plate 14, figures 32, 33)

A small specimen lacking the anterior and the posterior ends of carapace.   Carapace wide at middle, narrowing rapidly backward; postero-lateral region thick and rounded; traces of a marginal line on the left side.   Exposed surface covered with a pavement of fine depressed granules; two thumb-nail impressions at center of carapace deep; farther back a triangle of three granules, two arranged transversely, the third posterior and median; on anterior part a trace of a blunt median carina, and on either side a short, curved, oblique, impressed line concave forward.   Pterygostomian regions much swollen, crisply granulate.   First sternite large, broken, post-lateral lobes concave behind; anterior lobe intact, sharp at tip, anterior margins obliquely concave.   Second sternite narrow.   The basal articles of only the first two pereiopods are present.

Measurements: Greatest width of carapace, 8.7 millimeters; length (incomplete), 11 millimeters.

Occurrence: Texas: Tarrant County at Blue Mound, near Haslet; Denton clay, Cretaceous; 1920; W. S. Adkins and W. M. and Hortense T. Winton, collectors.

Collection: University of Texas, type, Coll. No. 284.

Raninella (?) *armata* Rathbun, n.sp.
(Plate 11, figures 32, 33)

A narrow abdomen widest at the middle, tapering to either end, and showing five armed segments of subequal length.   They may be considered Nos. 3–7; 5 and 6 widest, 4 a little narrower, 3 still narrower but broader than long, 7 narrowest, length and breadth subequal, subtriangular with rounded tip.   Each is armed with a stout conical median spine standing at right angles to the surface; of the spines 5 is longest, 4 and 6 next, 3 and 7 small; segments 4, 5, and 6 have also a small upstanding spine above lateral margins.   Otherwise the surface appears smooth.

[20] In allusion to the sharp-pointed sternum.

Owing to the usual absence of the abdomen from fossil Raninids, it is impossible to place this fragment with certainty.

Measurements: Greatest width of abdomen, 7 millimeters; length and width of terminal segment, 4.6 millimeters.

Occurrence: Texas: Blue Mound, near Haslet, Tarrant County; Denton clay; 1920; W. S. Adkins and W. M. and H. T. Winton, collectors; one specimen.

Collection: University of Texas, type, Coll. No. 284.

Raninella (?) starkvillensis Rathbun, n.sp.

(Plate 9, figures 4, 5)

A carpus or wrist of a right cheliped. An elongate swelling occupies the greater part of the outer surface, terminating distally in a round knob directed outward and bearing twelve tubercles. The remainder of the swelling is covered with larger tubercles of varying size and some granules, the largest tubercles forming a curved line of six on the lower border. The tubercles of the upper surface are mostly small. The condyle articulating with the merus is granulate. Length of carpus, 15.8 millimeters.

Occurrence: Mississippi: Gullies on campus of Agricultural and Mechanical College, Starkville, Oktibbeha County; Oktibbeha tongue of Selma chalk; November 7, 1903; A. F. Crider, collector (3186).

Collection: U. S. National Museum, type, Cat. No. 73831.

Genus NOTOSCELES Bourne
Notosceles bournei Rathbun

(Plate 26, figure 5)

1928. *Notosceles bournei.* Rathbun, U. S. Nat. Mus., Pr., vol. 73, art. 6, p. 1, pl. 1. Type-locality, Kerens, Navarro County, Texas; Midway, basal Eocene.

Occurrence: Texas, Elgin, Bastrop County; Navarro group, Upper Cretaceous.

Family ATELECYCLIDAE
Genus AVITELMESSUS Rathbun
Avitelmessus grapsoideus Rathbun

1923. *Avitelmessus grapsoideus.* Rathbun, N. C. Geol. and Econ. Surv., vol. 5, p. 404, pl. 101, pl. 102, fig. 4.
1926. *Avitelmessus grapsoideus.* Rathbun, *in* Bruce Wade, U. S. Geol. Surv., Prof. Pap. 137, p. 190, pls. 69 and 70.

Occurrence: North Carolina, Tennessee, Alabama, and Mississippi; Upper Cretaceous:

North Carolina: Peedee formation, near Hudlers Landing, Cape Fear River, 30½ miles above Wilmington (type-locality).

Tennessee: Ripley and Selma formations, Coon Creek region, McNairy County; Cat. Nos. 73122, 73453, 73701–73704, 73735.

Alabama: Ripley formation: Eufaula; L. C. Johnson, collector; Chattahoochee River between mouth of Cowikee Creek and Eufaula, and between Eufaula and Barbour Creek; T. W. Stanton, collector.

Mississippi: Ripley formation: Coon Creek tongue, cut of Southern Railway, three-quarters of a mile west of Wenasoga, Alcorn County, 1910, L. W. Stephenson, collector (6877); Cat. No. 73833. Bullocks old overshot mill bluff, Tippah County, Section 36, Township 5, Range 4 East, October 24, 1888, L. C. Johnson, collector

(542); Cat. No. 73732.   Bullocks old mill, 2 miles south of Dumas, October 22 and 26, 1889, T. W. Stanton, collector (708); Cat. No. 73719.   Crum's Mill, September, 1888, L. C. Johnson, collector (552); Cat. Nos. 73721, 73730.   E. Hatchie Creek, Crum's old mill site, 16½ miles northeast of Ripley, at base of section, 1909, L. W. Stephenson, collector (6462); Cat. No. 73720.   W. O'Kelly's farm, 2½ miles south of Dumas, T. W. Stanton, collector (709); Cat. No. 31896.   Hales Branch and Big Hatchie Creek, L. C. Johnson, collector (549), Cat. No. 73725.   Two miles northeast of Keownville, Union County (6873); Cat. No. 73734.   Aberdeen road 6½ miles southeast of Pontotoc, Pontotoc County, south side of creek at end of bridge, L. W. Stephenson, collector (6469); Cat. No. 73733.

Oktibbeha tongue of Selma chalk; gullies on campus of Agricultural and Mechanical College, Starkville, Oktibbeha County; 1910; L. W. Stephenson, collector (6844); one right immovable finger; Cat. No. 73839.

Collection: U. S. National Museum, type, Cat. No. 31895.

Family PORTUNIDAE

Genus OPHTHALMOPLAX Rathbun, n.gen.

Anterior margin nearly equal to greatest width of carapace; front occupying one-quarter of this margin. Orbits long. Carapace shield-shape, broadly rounded behind the orbital angles. Lateral spines few. Chelae spinous. Manus carinate.

Resembles *Carcineretes* Withers[21] in which the carapace is widest at the orbits and is devoid of spines and the chela not carinated. Akin to the Recent *Euphylax*,[22] but with wider front, orbital margin dentate instead of entire, chelae shorter. It also has a resemblance to *Lithophylax trigeri* A. Milne Edwards,[23] from the Cenomanian of France, a species with long eyes, which, however, has never been figured. The holotype is not to be found in the Paris Museum.[24]

Genotype: *O. stephensoni* Rathbun, n.sp.

Ophthalmoplax stephensoni Rathbun, n.sp.

(Plate 13, figures 13–18; Plate 26, figure 10)

Carapace of female one-fifth broader than long, convex, surface uneven. Two antero-lateral spines, the intervening space equal to that between the anterior spine and the tip of the orbital spine; the interspaces concave downward; the cross-section of the posterior or branchial spine is small, directed upward and slightly outward, of the anterior or hepatic spine larger, diameter more than twice as great, directed upward. Front between orbits four-spined, lateral spines conical, ascending obliquely forward; between them the surface is strongly deflexed, concave, medially furrowed, terminating in two stout, widely divergent spines, directed downward and outward. The orbit is divided into two unequal parts, the inner two-thirds as wide as the outer and separated from it by a prominent, blunt, obliquely compressed tooth; just inside this tooth there is a deep,

---

[21] Thomas H. Withers: *On a new brachyurous crustacean from the upper Cretaceous of Jamaica*, Ann. Mag. Nat. Hist., ser. 9, vol. 10 (1922) pls. 16 and 17.

[22] W. Stimpson: *Notes on North American crustacea, in the Museum of the Smithsonian Institution*, no. II, Ann. Lyc. Nat. Hist. New York, vol. 7 (1860) p. 225 [97], pl. 3, fig. 5.

[23] A. Milne Edwards: *Additions à la famille des Thalassiniens*, Soc. Philom., Bull., ser. 7, vol. 3 (1879) p. 117.

[24] According to M. Boule and C. Gravier.

closed, buttonhole fissure.   The margins of the outer frontal tooth and of the orbit as far as the fissure are marked by a single row of granules.   The outer cavity of the orbit is bordered by a broad, triangular tooth with a granulated outer line and a narrower tooth at the outer angle; both are produced forward and slightly upward.   Eyes lacking.   The ventral surface of the carapace is detached from the dorsal.   The lower orbital region shows the greater part of the margin which has three finely granulated teeth or spines corresponding in relative position to those of the upper margin.   Immediately below the teeth there is a deep groove narrow at the inner end and widening as the groove curves downward and outward. Below the outer two-fifths of the groove there is a finely granulated ridge, two or three granules wide, which may serve as a stridulating ridge.   The gastric region is not divided into subregions; across its widest part there is a high ridge armed with three distant spines; on the hind part is a shorter, lower ridge with no spines in evidence.   The hepatic region delimited by a broad shallow depression leading back from the orbital sinus, is subquadrilateral and embraces the first lateral spine.   The surface of the cardiac region is not exposed; an almost transverse furrow leads from it across the branchial region to the lateral margin.   The slope downward from the antero-lateral margin is nearly vertical and partially recessive; from the postero-lateral margin it is anteriorly steep but flattens out toward the posterior margin; the latter is thick and granulated.

On the sternum, which is out of its normal position, there is a strong spine at the base of the cheliped, directed downward; the anterior angle of the same segment has a granulated carina on either side; behind this there is a granulated elevation either side of the tip of the abdominal cavity.   The oviducal aperture on the next segment is of small size.

Maxillipeds lacking.   Chelipeds massive, of moderate length, the right somewhat the larger.   The ischium shows three spines on the ventral surface, two across the distal part, one smaller at proximal end; and three strong spines on the anterior margin.   Merus stout, two spines far apart on the thick lower margin.   Palms subequal, nearly as broad as long; four blunt carinae in outer view, one on upper margin spinous; the next is at the level of the articulating condyle of the dactylus and is short and seemingly unarmed; the next is in line with the interdigital sinus and has a few large spines; the lower margin has smaller but more numerous spines.   The manus is subtruncate below; its inner margin has at least three small spines (on the proximal half); a second row through the middle of the inner surface is indicated by two on a blunt ridge at the distal two-fifths of the surface. Propodal finger compressed, a shallow longitudinal groove outside above the lower margin; lower margin with five (or more) spines in continuation of those on the manus; on the prehensile edge, four or more tubercles diminishing in size.   Dactylus thick, a shallow punctate groove through the middle of inner surface, three or more large irregular spines on upper surface, and two small spines or tubercles on the inner slope of the proximal spine; on the prehensile edge, three or more tubercles diminishing in size. Ischium of first ambulatory leg with a spine at each of the distal corners of the lower surface.

Measurements (approximate): Female holotype, median length of carapace, 65.6 millimeters; greatest width, behind middle, 87.6 millimeters; width between outer angles of orbits, 65.4 millimeters; length of right manus to interdigital sinus, 29 millimeters; greatest height, 24 millimeters. Largest specimen (K 512), length of carapace, 98.6 millimeters; width, 110 millimeters.

Occurrence:

South Carolina: Davis Landing, right bank, Peedee River; Peedee formation; L. W. Stephenson, collector; one left chela; Cat. No. 73794.

Alabama: Lowndes County, in cut of Louisville and Nashville Railroad, 1⅜ miles north of Fort Deposit; Ripley formation; L. W. Stephenson, collector (6783); one right chela; Cat. No. 73795.

Mississippi: Union County, on land of J. A. Roberts, 5½ miles east of New Albany and a few rods north of New Albany and Baldwin road at "The Caves"; Ripley formation; near base of sector, loose in ravine; L. W. Stephenson, collector (6466g); May, 1909; one female, holotype.

Collection: U. S. National Museum, type, Cat. No. 73793.

Texas: Arroyo Toro Colorado, one mile down the Rio Grande from Las Isletas, southern Maverick County; Upper Cretaceous; W. F. Cummins, W. Kennedy, and J. M. Sands, collectors; thirteen specimens.

Collection: University of Texas, K 512.

Zanthopsis brasiliana Maury[25] from the State of Parahyba do Norte, Maestrichtian stage of upper Cretaceous, belongs to the genus *Ophthalmoplax*. The carapace is more swollen laterally than in *O. stephensoni* and is provided with two strong postlateral spines, the true postlateral margin being concealed.

Ophthalmoplax comancheensis Rathbun, n.sp.

(Plate 13, figures 1–5)

1928. *Callianassa?* sp. Adkins, Univ. Texas, Bull. 2838, p. 83.

Represented by fingers which resemble those of *O. stephensoni* more than any other Cretaceous species. The least worn specimen, a right dactylus, is made the type. It is incomplete at both ends. Length four times greatest height; inner and outer surfaces with a deep, broad, longitudinal furrow, reaching nearly to distal end. Dactylus moderately curved upward lengthwise, upper surface obliquely convex transversely, sloping downward on outer side where it forms a blunt carina above the furrow. Surface roughened with fine granules and some larger granules or tubercles:

[25] C. J. Maury: *O cretaceo da Parahyba do Norte*, Servico Geologico Mineralogico do Brasil, Mon. 8 (1930) p. 111, pl. 4, figs. 1 and 2.

four or five tubercles on proximal half of outer carina; five in the distal three-fifths of the middle line of upper surface; a few smaller scattered tubercles. Prehensile teeth low, one large at proximal end, followed by three small and widely spaced.

Three other dactyls were taken at as many different points. The largest lacks its distal two-fifths but shows the scars of four carinal tubercles. A small specimen has a slender, blunt tip, with a prehensile tooth at a short distance; surface densely granulate, without the tubercles of the type, but with a conical tubercle at the proximal end of its upper surface. No other specimen shows this feature, as the end of the finger or the tubercle itself has been destroyed. A similar tubercle is prominent in *O. stephensoni*. The smallest dactyl is still slenderer, tip lacking.

A left immobile finger is of good size, is curved strongly inward, and armed on the prehensile margin with a large and long, flat-topped basal tooth, followed by two successively smaller triangular teeth; tip obliquely upturned. A longitudinal furrow on outer and inner surfaces, broad at proximal end, narrowing to a point toward the tip. On outer surface a band of fine punctae below the teeth.

Measurements: Approximate length of dactylus, holotype, 2.3 millimeters; greatest height, 6 millimeters. Approximate length of fixed finger, paratype, 20.3 millimeters; height 7.7 millimeters.

Occurrence: Texas; Cretaceous:

Grayson County: 3 miles north of Denison, south bank of Duck Creek, 40 feet above base of Kde type-locality; in marl above *Pervinquieria* aff. *trinodosa;* one left dactyl, one right immobile finger, paratype; W. S. Adkins, collector (211).

Tarrant County: Sycamore Creek valley, 3± miles southeast of Fort Worth, at pit of Cobb brickyards (= quarter of a mile east of Sycamore Creek); Pawpaw clay; one right dactyl and fragment of another; W. S. Adkins, collector (196).

Tarrant County: 4½ miles southeast of Fort Worth, quarter of a mile south of International Great Northern Railway bridge across Sycamore Creek; Pawpaw clay; one left dactyl and the proximal end, with large tooth, of five large fingers; W. S. Adkins, collector (209).

Tarrant County: Sycamore Creek valley, 4½± miles southeast of Fort Worth and half a mile northeast of loc. 209; Pawpaw clay; one right dactyl, holotype; W. S. Adkins, collector.

Collection: University of Texas, type, Coll. No. 244.

Family XANTHIDAE
Genus ACTAEA DeHaan
Actaea cretacea Rathbun, n.sp.

(Plate 9, figure 3)

Holotype; a right palm and immobile finger. Palm short and stout, upper and lower lines slightly arcuate, proximal margin oblique, distal margin vertical at articulation of dactylus; outer surface curving inward above and below to the plane of the inner surface, which is comparatively flat and uneven. Outer surface of palm coarsely and irregularly granulate, about twelve granules in the longest longitudinal row and approximately fourteen rows. Granulation of inner surface finer and more obscure. Finger short, triangular, curving inward; deeply grooved, two grooves inside and outside, the interspaces swollen, subcylindrical, terminating each in a short triangular prehensile tooth. A smaller tooth close to palm; finger tip produced obliquely upward. A shallow furrow followed by punctae on the inner part of lower surface of finger.

Paratype, a right palm without finger.

Measurements of holotype: Greatest length of palm and finger, 6.8

millimeters; length of palm from proximal lower angle to distal end above finger, 4.8 millimeters; greatest height of palm, 3.7 millimeters; length of finger, 2 millimeters; height of finger at base, 1.5 millimeters.

Occurrence: Texas: Tarrant County, $4\frac{1}{2}$ miles southeast of Fort Worth, quarter of a mile south of International Great Northern Railway bridge across Sycamore Creek; Pawpaw clay; W. S. Adkins, collector.

Collection: University of Texas, types, Coll. No. 209.

Genus CALOXANTHUS A. Milne Edwards
Caloxanthus americanus Rathbun, n.sp.
(Plate 11, figures 12–19)

The type is a small carapace, two-thirds as long as wide; anterior half, strongly swollen; posterior half flatter and narrowing to the posterior margin, which is about half as wide as the carapace. Fronto-orbital width a little more than two-thirds the carapace width. Very little of the outer layer of the surface remains; it is white and punctate, the punctae rimmed; they are larger anteriorly, suboval, and not contiguous, posteriorly smaller and nearer; a row of minute punctae on posterior margin; a smooth furrow behind orbital margin. Antero-lateral margin rounding gradually into postero-lateral, edge finely punctate, as also the ventral surface of the carapace and exposed surface of abdomen. Epistome punctate, the raised margins between the antennular cavities finely so; also the transverse edge of the basal article of the antennules. Edge of front broken off. The layers below the outer one on the carapace appear to have oval tubercles with a hollow center; the mesogastric region is faintly defined, the cardiac more deeply so; it has two tubercles transversely placed, and behind it a smaller median one. Pterygostomian region with a narrow swelling below orbit and following the line of the suture.

Buccal cavity subcircular, broader in anterior half; the epistome curves backward toward the median line. The terminal segment of the abdomen (♀ ?) is triangular, broader than long.

With the single carapace are various parts of chelipeds. Manus short, higher than wide, less than twice as long through the middle as high; swollen, upper and lower margins not compressed, arcuate; a broad shallow depression on inner surface below middle; a sinus below insertion of fixed finger; distal end of palm oblique, proximal end slightly concave, almost transverse. Surface of manus, carpus, and merus coarsely and densely granulate. Fingers moderately deflexed, slender, equally thick, and high, length unknown; a deep longitudinal groove on the inner and the outer surfaces, the upper surface of dactylus and the lower surface of immobile finger; prehensile edges armed with separated tubercles. Wrist subcylindrical, about as broad as long; the innermost surface of the flexed arm is flat as though fitting close to the body and not extending beyond it.

Measurements: Length of carapace of holotype, 5.3 millimeters; width, 7.7 millimeters; fronto-orbital width, 5.5 millimeters; posterior width, 3.7 millimeters. Length of palm of a paratype through middle, 6.5 millimeters; height, 3.6 millimeters; thickness, 3.2 millimeters; height of each finger at base, 1 millimeter; thickness at base, 1.2 millimeters.

Relation: This species has much in common with the type species of the genus, *C. formosus* A. Milne Edwards,[26] from the greensand of the Maine (Cenomanian), which, however, has the carapace covered with tubercles instead of punctae and placed close together; the posterior margin is narrower, about one-third width of carapace.

Occurrence: Texas, Tarrant County; Pawpaw clay:

Four miles southwest of Fort Worth, half a mile south of Baptist Seminary; one misshapen carapace, three specimens of palm, one with wrist; W. S. Adkins and W. M. Winton, collectors.

Southeast of Fort Worth, 4½ miles, quarter of a mile south of International Great Northern Railway bridge across Sycamore Creek; one carapace, holotype, twelve palms, four with fingers, two with wrists, one with arm; W. S. Adkins, collector.

Collection: University of Texas, type, Coll. No. 209.

Genus MENIPPE DeHaan
Menippe cretacea Rathbun, n.sp.
(Plate 13, figures 7, 8)

Two large right fingers, mobile and immobile, perhaps not from the same specimen. Immobile finger (holotype) with lower margin nearly straight until near distal end where it slopes slightly upward (tip broken off). Prehensile edge thick, its inner surface curved strongly inward at base, cutting edge with six lobiform teeth; the one at middle is largest and most striking, its distal margin upright or at right angles to lower margin of finger, its proximal margin horizontal. Behind are three low teeth, two small near proximal end of finger, the third larger. On distal half are two teeth of which the distal one is small, the other large with subrectangular margins and lower down than the largest tooth.

Dactylus with upper margin strongly arched in profile and curved inward. On outer surface an impressed line of punctae a little below middle. Prehensile margin horizontal for proximal half and provided with seven low, unequal teeth; two near proximal end are united at base and followed by a triangular notch and tooth; remaining teeth insignificant.

A specimen from Mississippi, showing distal half of immobile finger, may belong here; it has the larger rectangular prehensile tooth followed by

---

[26] A. Milne Edwards: *Monographie des crustacés fossiles de la famille des cancériens*, Ann. Sci. Nat., Zool., ser. 4, vol. 20 (1863) p. 282, pl. 9, figs. 1–1d; ser. 5, vol. 1 (1864) p. 44.

only one low tooth, a row of punctae below the middle of the outer surface, and the finger gradually ascending near the tip.

Measurements: Fixed finger, estimated length, 26 millimeters; basal height, 12.8 millimeters. Dactyl, length, 33.6 millimeters; basal height, 12.4 millimeters.

Occurrence:

Texas: Timber Creek, 4 miles due west of Lewisville, Denton County, and a few hundred yards below a road bridge; Woodbine formation, upper Cretaceous; 1911; L. W. Stephenson, collector (7552); two specimens, holotype and paratype.

Mississippi: Gullies on Aiken farm about $2\frac{1}{3}$ miles north of Starkville, Oktibbeha County; Oktibbeha tongue of Selma chalk; L. W. Stephenson, collector (6845); one specimen; Cat. No. 73787.

Collection: U. S. National Museum, types, Cat. No. 73827.

Family MAJIDAE
Genus STENOCIONOPS (Leach ms.) Desmarest
Stenocionops primus Rathbun, n.sp.

(Plate 13, figures 9–12)

The proximal portion of a right manus, about two-thirds as thick as its width at middle, a widening from the proximal to the distal end; outer surface longitudinally a little convex, inner surface more convex; constricted near the carpal articulation. Upper and lower margins broadly rounded from side to side; a shallow furrow on each side a little below the upper margin, the inner one ends proximally in a deep hollow. Surface tuberculate and granulate, the tubercles more prominent on the inner surface and arranged largely in rows, about five rows outside, four inside, three above; the outer tubercles are less prominent than the inner and upper; the most prominent tubercle is one at the proximal end of a row through the middle of the inner surface.

Measurements: Length of the fragment, 33.4 millimeters; width at middle, 14.7 millimeters, thickness at middle, 11.2 millimeters.

Remarks: In shape, this manus bears a strong resemblance to that of the Recent *S. furcata* (Olivier),[27] which is not so thick, is more finely roughened, and perhaps considerably longer.

Occurrence: Arkansas: Old road half a mile south of Buckrange, Howard County; bed of glauconitic sand in Brownstown formation, upper Cretaceous; 1925; Carl H. Dane, collector (13451); holotype.

Collection: U. S. National Museum, type, Cat. No. 73838.

---

[27] M. J. Rathbun: *The spider crabs of America*, U. S. Nat. Mus., Bull. 129 (1925) p. 449, pls. 160 and 161, text-fig. 131.

Order ISOPODA
Family AEGIDAE
Palaega guadalupensis Rathbun, n.sp.
(Plate 12, figures 3, 4)

Represented chiefly by the abdomen. Surface covered with reticulating punctae visible to the naked eye. First five segments of subequal length (in the direction of the axis of the animal); epimeron of fifth segment scythe-shaped, twice as long as broad at base, projecting laterally beyond the line of the telson. Telson nearly as broad as its length plus the length of the fifth segment; sides of anterior half, slightly convergent; posterior half, semicircular; posterior third, margined with triangular spines; a strong blunt median carina beginning near the anterior end and diminishing in width and height posteriorly. Some fragments of thoracic segments indicate that they are little longer than those of the abdomen, and their epimera are triangular, pointed, and do not extend laterally beyond the succeeding one.

Measurements: Length of abdominal segments 1–5 inclusive, 13.4 millimeters; length of telson, 19.3 millimeters; width of same, 21.6 millimeters.

Relation: This species is allied to *P. carteri* Woodward,[28] the type of the genus. It also has a strong resemblance to the genus *Bathynomus*,[29] but until the anterior end is known, its relation will remain problematic.

Occurrence: Texas; Upper Cretaceous:

Guadalupe River, a few hundred yards above International Great Northern Railroad bridge, one mile east of New Braunfels, Comal County; Taylor marl; 1911; L. W. Stephenson, collector (7625); holotype and impression.

In bed of Salado Creek, one mile below crossing of Austin road, about 3.5 miles east of north of Alamo Heights, Bexar County; Austin chalk; 1911; L. W. Stephenson, collector (7650); a fragment showing portions of seven thoracic segments of a larger specimen than the holotype; average length of segments, 3 millimeters; Cat. No. 73844.

Collection: U. S. National Museum, type, Cat. No. 73845.

Palaega williamsonensis Rathbun, n.sp.
(Plate 12, figures 1, 2)

A parasitic form showing the abdomen and three segments of the thorax. The width equals about the length of the telson and the adjoining segment. Surface covered with large, reticulating punctae; epimera, where present,

---

[28] H. Woodward: *Contributions to British fossil crustacea*, Geol. Mag., vol. 7 (1870) p. 496, pl. 22, figs. 3–6.

[29] A. Milne Edwards: *Isopode gigantesque des grandes profondeurs de la mer*, Compt. Rend., vol. 89 (1879) p. 21.

reaching well backward beyond the terga.   The thoracic segments diminish in length (axial) toward the abdomen; the two anterior abdominal segments are shorter than the remainder.   The telson has been folded so as to form a longitudinal carina and a groove, neither of which is median and, therefore, accidental; posterior margin armed with about 24 minute spines. Resembles *P. scrobiculata* Ammon[30] from the lower Oligocene of the Tyrol.

Measurements: Length of specimen (incomplete), 26.5 millimeters; greatest width, about 11 millimeters.

Occurrence: Texas; Navarro formation: Williamson County, 2½ miles southwest of Thrall; September 11; L. W. Stephenson, W. P. Popenoe, and J. A. Gardner, collectors; type and reverse.

Collection: U. S. National Museum, type, Cat. No. 73796.

UNDETERMINED SPECIMENS OF DECAPODA PREVIOUSLY RECORDED

"*Astacus*, sp."

Morton, Am. Jour. Sci., vol. 17 (1830) p. 287.

Upper Cretaceous; ferruginous sand formation.   Delaware; in digging Chesapeake and Delaware Canal. In Philadelphia Academy, "almost entire."

Palm, undetermined

"Leg joint," Weller, N. J. Geol. Surv., Paleont. ser., vol. 4 (1907) pl. 110, fig. 11.

Cretaceous: Merchantville clay-marl.   Lenola, New Jersey.

Antenna of Palinurid

"Brachyura (?).   Fragment of a finger (?)."   Pilsbry, Philadelphia Acad. Nat. Sci., Pr. (1901) p. 117, pl. 1, fig. 17.

Cretaceous: Lower marl beds.   Monmouth County, New Jersey.

"Crab"

R. T. Hill, U. S. Geol. Surv., 21st Ann. Rept., 1899–1900, part 7 (1901) p. 302.

On fossil log in greensand of Woodbine formation of Lamar County, Texas.

"Indeterminate limb segments"

Adkins, Univ. Texas, Bull. 1856 (1918) p. 62.

Goodland formation.   Texas.

"Lobster related to Homarus"

Adkins, Univ. Texas, Bull. 1856 (1918) p. 62.

Fort Worth limestone.   Texas.

"Crustacean chela"

Winton, Univ. Texas, Bull. 2544 (1925) p. 71, pl. 15, fig. 2.

Comanche series.   Texas.

---

[30] L. von Ammon: *Ein Beitrag zur Kenntniss der vorweltlichen Asseln,* Sitzungsb. math.-phys. Cl. k. b. Akad. Wiss. München, vol. 12 (1882) p. 519, pls. 1–4.

EOCENE

Order DECAPODA

Family HOMARIDAE
Genus HOPLOPARIA McCoy
Hoploparia johnsoni Rathbun n.sp.

(Plate 14, figures 25-31)

Four animals all incomplete. The largest one shows a stout carapace much swollen at the middle, where it is just as wide as high. The sutures are disposed much as in typical *Hoploparia*.[31] Only one suture crosses the median line of the dorsum; it is deep, curving slightly backward above, and ending at the lower third of the height of the carapace. In front of, and parallel to, the lower part there is a second shorter deep suture which forks at its lower end, the anterior branch curving forward subparallel to the lower margin of carapace, the posterior branch connected by a shallow furrow with the dorsal suture. The sides of the carapace are densely covered with small, rounded, rather depressed tubercles directed forward; toward the upper surface the tubercles take on the aspect of hair sockets and become transverse, almost linear, and farther apart. The front edge of the carapace is lacking. A row of three spines is visible, leading toward the antennal spine; the hinder of the three lies between the transverse sutures. There is at least one spine on the lateral ridge leading to the rostrum.

The pleuron of the first abdominal segment has a broadly rounded lateral margin; that of the second segment is subquadrilateral with the postero-lateral angle drawn to an acuminate spine; the next three pleura are subtriangular, higher than long, terminating in an acute angle. The surface of all is rather coarsely punctate; dorsal surface of abdomen sparingly covered with short, linear, transverse punctae.

Palm elongated, thick through the middle, greatest height a little more than half as long as length to sinus, increasing in height from proximal to distal end. Upper and lower margins slightly arcuate, upper margin bluntly rounded, armed toward the inner surface with a row of four spines, three of good size, the proximal spine small; lower margin broad, subtruncate, defined on the inside by a narrow groove. Inner and outer surfaces each with a spine near the distal end and midway of the height. General surface covered with small, roundish sockets, arranged in transverse wavy lines; between these rows are smaller punctae or sockets. Fingers long,

---

[31] F. McCoy: *On the classification of some British fossil crustacea, with notices of new forms in the University Collection at Cambridge*, Ann. Mag. Nat. Hist., ser. 2, vol. 4 (1849) p. 175, text-figures.

compressed, gradually tapering, armed on the prehensile edges with unequal lobiform teeth, some compressed, others depressed. At the base of the dactylus on the inner side, at the articulation, a strong outstanding spine or tubercle with tip broken off and on the outer side of the upper margin a tubercle. Carpus with a narrow acuminate spine at inner distal angle; two other spines are visible on the surface.

Differs from *H. gabbi*,[32] which is known only from chelae, carpus and part of an abdomen, in the palm longer, narrower at proximal end, less swollen, lower edge truncate rather than rounded, a distal spine on inside as well as outside surface, and the abdomen with fewer and more distant punctae.

H. tennesseensis[33] has short swollen palms, a deep groove along the lower margin of palm and fingers, a row of three spines on inner side of proximal three-fifths of upper margin and one spine at proximal end of outer side of same margin, and no spine on inner or outer surface of manus. The margin of the pleura of the abdominal segments is thick and set off by a correspondingly deep furrow.

H. mcnairyensis[34] has the carapace covered with distant beadlike tubercles of similar size.

Measurements: Width of carapace of type-specimen, 22.7 millimeters; median length of carapace behind cervical suture, 16.2 millimeters. Largest manus, right, length through middle, 32 millimeters; distal width, 18.4 millimeters; proximal width, 10 millimeters.

Occurrence: Alabama: Prairie Creek and Pine Barren section, Wilcox County; Sucarnoochee beds, Midway, lower Eocene; L. C. Johnson, collector (264, 284); four badly mutilated animals, the largest the type; twelve hands, two with wrists attached, six fragments of fingers; Cat. Nos. 371517–371520.

Collection: U. S. National Museum; type, Cat. No. 371518.

Genus NEPHROPSIS Wood-Mason
Nephropsis midwayensis Rathbun, n.sp.

(Plate 16, figures 3–5)

A left chela with a piece of the carpus attached. A spine has been broken off from the carpus at the swollen inner articulation with the manus, also another spine from the upper distal extremity of the carpus. Manus thick, half as thick as high; superior length little greater than height; a spine indicated at distal outer corner above. Propodal finger at base over half the height of the palm, rapidly diminishing, inclined somewhat downward, upper margin oblique; a large conical spine near base, and directed distad

---

[32] For synonymy, see under "Cretaceous."
[33] For synonymy, see under "Cretaceous."
[34] For synonymy, see under "Cretaceous."

and outward.   Dactylus arcuate above, margins obscure, a low swelling on inner surface at base.   Both fingers are swollen, an indication that they may be spooned.   On the outer surface of the palm a broad shallow, smooth, longitudinal furrow below upper margin and another above lower margin.   The remainder of the palmar surface is covered with granules, each imbedded in a socket and directed distad.

Measurements: Holotype, length of palm on upper margin, 9.4 millimeters; height at middle, 9 millimeters; thickness, 4.6 millimeters.

Occurrence: Alabama: Pine Barren section, Wilcox County; Sucarnoochee beds, Midway, lower Eocene; L. C. Johnson, collector (Coll. No. (284).

Collection: U. S. National Museum, type, Cat. No. 371741.

Genus ISCHNODACTYLUS Pelseneer

Ischnodactylus cookei Rathbun, n.sp.

(Plate 14, figures 1-6)

Based on specimens of the manus with the stump of the fixed finger. Palm much swollen, thickness two-thirds of the width, width about two-thirds of the length.   Proximal end lacking in all specimens.   The greatest width is probably near middle of palm.   Surface smooth, without carinae or granulation.   The lower margin is indicated by a row of more than twelve fine punctae on the palm, the row continued on the finger.   A row of more distant punctae marks the   upper margin, but it is situated a little to the inside of the middle of the smoothly rounded upper surface. Various other punctae are scattered on outer and inner surfaces, one scant row below the middle of the outer surface, and two irregular rows on the upper half of the inner surface.   An almost imperceptible furrow on the inner side just below the upper surface.   The immovable finger is strongly deflexed, its lower margin forming a broad sinus with that of the palm; it is slender, its cross-section 2 millimeters from its origin subcircular, measuring $1\frac{2}{3}$ millimeter in a vertical direction, $1\frac{1}{3}$ millimeter horizontally; on the prehensile edge of this stump is a threadlike carina bearing four tiny impressions representing spines followed by a much larger base of a spine.

A fragment of a finger from a different locality in Alabama to the type lot is slender, subcylindrical, gradually tapering.   The prehensile surface has a slight carina closely set with a single row of short, conical spines, the larger ones separated by several (two to four) smaller ones.   On either side of the carina there is an irregular row of small punctae.   On the opposite side of the finger from the spines there is a shallow furrow containing a row of punctae, and on either side a row of somewhat larger and fewer punctae. The punctae are all in the nature of hair sockets and trend distad.   This finger is referred tentatively to *I. cookei*.   It is the only one found similar in caliber and spination to that indicated by the basal portion of the type-specimen.

Measurements: The holotype which has the longest piece of finger attached is about 8.3 millimeters high. A more complete specimen is 7.7 millimeters high, the largest 11.5 millimeters high. The isolated finger is, at the larger end, one millimeter in horizontal diameter and slightly greater in vertical diameter.

Occurrence:

Alabama: Prairie Creek region, Wilcox County; Sucarnoochee beds, Midway, lower Eocene; L. C. Johnson, collector (Coll. No. 264); eleven specimens of manus, of which one is holotype.

Alabama: Estelle, Wilcox County; Sucarnoochee beds; one fragment of finger (Alabama Mus. Nat. Hist.).

Collections: U. S. National Museum, type, Cat. No. 371512; Alabama Museum of Natural History.

Ischnodactylus cookei lowei Rathbun, n.subsp.

Two incomplete specimens of manus, one with the stump of fixed finger attached. Of the same general appearance as typical *cookei*. Differences: Color whitish shaded with blue, in a limestone instead of clay matrix; punctae on lower margin of palm slightly farther apart; sinus below distal end of palm less high; lower margin of propodus with less tendency to form a carina.

Occurrence:

Mississippi: Yazoo City, Yazoo County, in large ravine below old reservoir, about one mile south of Yazoo and Mississippi Valley Railroad station, along street-car line; Jackson formation, upper Eocene; October 11, 1912; E. N. Lowe and C. W. Cooke, collectors (Coll. No. 6472); two specimens of manus; height 11 millimeters.

Collection: U. S. National Museum; type, Cat. No. 371511.

Ischnodactylus cultellus Rathbun, n.sp.

(Plate 14, figures 7–12)

Portion of four fingers; one at least, the holotype, is a dactylus (right) and shows the articulating end; except at the base the finger is slender, viewed laterally, and increases gradually in height from the proximal end; it is thin in dorsal view and is drawn to an edge above and below; the finger is slightly arcuate outward, and the upper margin arcuate upward, the lower margin straight. Inner and outer surfaces smooth and shining. Prehensile edge armed with eight larger unequal spines and about fifteen smaller ones; all but a few are broken off, and they are short. Either side of the spines there is a row of punctae; a row of seven larger punctae either side of the upper margin; a median row of eight on inner surface; a few additional scattered punctae. Adjacent to the articulation the finger widens horizontally, forming a strong, triangular base, seen from above.

A second specimen, half as long as the holotype, is also basal; a third one, which represents the immovable finger (right), enlarges vertically as well as horizontally at the base, which is narrower than that of the dactylus; it is slightly concave below and is drawn to a sharp edge throughout its length; a row of thirteen sockets on the inner surface close to the lower edge, a row of eight punctae on the same surface at its lower third; a row either side of the prehensile spines; on the outer surface a row of five punctae a little above the lower edge. Prehensile edge straight, armed with eighteen spines, three of which are considerably larger than the others.

Measurements: Holotype, dactylus, length (end lacking), 13.6 millimeters; greatest height, 1.7 millimeters; width at articulation, 3 millimeters; height at articulation, 1.3 millimeters; width of blade, 0.5 millimeter. Paratype, propodal finger, length (end lacking), 8.6 millimeters; height at middle, 1.4 millimeters; width at articulation, about 2 millimeters; height at articulation, 2.4 millimeters; width of blade, 0.5 millimeter.

Remarks: The attachment of the dactylus to the propodus is similar to that of *I. macrodactylus* (Schlüter).[35] The isolated fingers might easily be mistaken for dorsal fin bones of a Cyprinodont.[36]

Occurrence: Alabama: Estelle, Wilcox County; Sucarnoochee beds, Midway, lower Eocene; holotype in Alabama Museum of Natural History.

Mississippi: Dry Creek, Jackson, Hinds County; Eocene; basal half of two fingers; loaned by E. W. Berry.

Collections: Alabama Museum of Natural History, type; Johns Hopkins University.

Ischnodactylus (?) *dentatus* Rathbun, n.sp.

(Plate 14, figures 19–22)

Three fragments of slender fingers may be referred to this genus. The longest, a right fixed finger, is 11 millimeters long by 1.8 millimeters in its widest part. Surface smooth and shining. Outer margin slightly sinuous, prehensile margin uneven, in general tapering distally. Finger slightly curved or arched outward, subcylindrical except for the prehensile teeth which are close together, number about thirty, and are low, triangular, thick, and unequal; three at equidistant intervals are larger than the others. On the outer surface near the lower border there is a row of eight rather large punctae unevenly spaced; near the prehensile border numerous small punctae which range roughly in two rows. On the lower border a row of sixteen elongate punctae. The inner surface has on its lower half twelve

---

[35] *See Hoploparia longimana.* C. Schlüter: *Die macruren decapoden der Senon- und Cenoman-Bildungen Westphalens,* Zeitschr. d. deutschen Geol. Ges., vol. 14 (1862) pl. 11, fig. 5.

[36] *See Fritsch on Ischnodactylus (= Stenocheles) esocinus* in A. Fritsch and J. Kafka: *Die Crustaceen d. böhm. Kreideformation* (1887) p. 40.

punctae alternating in two rows; on the upper half the punctae are smaller and more numerous.   All the punctae have the appearance of hair sockets.

Two shorter specimens show more clearly the proximal end of the dentate edge; the nine most proximal teeth are smaller than all others.

Occurrence: Mississippi: Eocene, probably lower; Dry Creek, Jackson, Hinds County; loaned by E. W. Berry.

Collection: Johns Hopkins University.

Ischnodactylus (?) sp.

(Plate 14, figures 23, 24)

A single right manus with the stump of a slender immovable finger is placed tentatively in this genus.   Proximal end of manus wanting.   Thickness of palm more than half as great as height; upper and lower surfaces wide and smoothly rounded; inner surface nearly as swollen as outer and with a slight depression in the upper proximal quarter.   Upper and lower margins arcuate; propodal finger inclined obliquely downward and inward, its base occupying only one-third of the distal height.   The dactylar opening diminishes in width toward the lower end.   The surface is smooth, showing only some obscure wavy transverse markings.

Measurements: Distal height of manus, 6.5 millimeters; greatest thickness, 3.6 millimeters.

Occurrence: Alabama; Prairie Creek, Wilcox County; Sucarnoochee beds, Midway; L. C. Johnson, collector (264); one specimen; Cat. No. 371514.

Collection: U. S. National Museum.

Family CALLIANASSIDAE
Genus UPOGEBIA Leach
Upogebia midwayensis Rathbun, n.sp.

(Plate 16, figures 1, 2)

The holotype consists of an abdomen of which segments 2–6 are in place, though incomplete, and a portion of the tail fan, out of place.   Segment 2 is one-third longer than No. 3, No. 4 a trifle longer than No. 3, No. 5 shorter than either, No. 6 longer than No. 2.   The pleura of Nos. 2–5 are longer in the direction of the axis of the shrimp than wide.   The pleura of segments 3 and 4 are set off from the terga by a blunt ridge which terminates anteriorly in each case in a smooth tubercle.   The pleura of Nos. 4 and 5 are each sculptured by a subquadrilateral furrow; a transverse punctate carina borders the anterior side of this furrow on No. 4; No. 6 has a series of linear punctate carinae on each side; two carinae are transverse and parallel on the lower part of the hinder half; the third carina is arched obliquely across the anterior corner.   Length of segments 2–6, about 39 millimeters.

Occurrence: Alabama: Pine Barren section, Wilcox County; Sucarnoochee beds, Midway; L. C. Johnson, collector (Coll. No. 284).
Collection: U. S. National Museum; type, Cat. No. 371516.

Genus CALLIANASSA Leach
Callianassa alpha Rathbun, n.sp.

(Plate 15, figures 23–25, 27)

Known from the propodus of the major cheliped and a portion of a minor chela of the first pair. Major palm a little longer than high, outer surface moderately convex in a vertical direction, inner surface much flatter; outer surface bent over inward at the top and forming a sharp and nearly horizontal carina; on the inner surface just below the carina there is normally a row of 17 to 24 punctae forming an irregular row; the lower surface is drawn to a sharp carina through its middle, which is marked with about 40 small crowded punctae in the largest specimen. Propodal finger slender, curving gradually upward and inward; the inferior carina is continued on the finger, becoming less sharp; the punctae which follow it are fewer and well spaced. The prehensile surface has a sharp submedian carina a little nearer the outer than the inner surface; at the basal end of the prehensile surface on either side there is a thickening or excrescence densely punctate and continued obliquely upward and backward on the palm. Otherwise, the propodus is smooth except for a few scattered punctae. The minor chela is narrow, elongate, about one-third as wide as the major; the fingers are more than three times as long as wide.

The punctate excrescences at the base of the finger are sufficient to identify specimens of this species.

Measurements: Holotype, length of palm at middle, 6.8 millimeters; height of same, 5.7 millimeters; thickness of same, 2.3 millimeters; height of finger at base up to the dactylar cavity, 2 millimeters. Largest palm, paratype, approximate length, 9.5 millimeters; height, 8.2 millimeters; thickness, 3.7 millimeters.

Occurrence:

Alabama: Prairie Creek region, Wilcox County; Sucarnoochee beds, Midway, lower Eocene; L. C. Johnson, collector (Coll. No. 264); 11 specimens.

Collection: U. S. National Museum; type, Cat. No. 371506.

Callianassa alpha Rathbun, var.

(Plate 15, figures 26, 28, 29)

Varies from the type lot as follows: Only nine punctae on the inner surface of the palm just below the superior carina; on the oblong excrescence either side of the basal portion of the finger the ornamentation appears more like low granules than punctae.   Length of palm, 11 millimeters; height, 8.5 millimeters; thickness, 4 millimeters.

Occurrence:

Mississippi: Large ravine below old reservoir at Yazoo City, Yazoo County, about one mile south of Yazoo and Mississippi Valley Railroad station, along street-car line; Jackson formation, upper Eocene; October 11, 1912; E. N. Lowe and C. W. Cooke, collectors (Coll. No. 6472); one left palm (Cat. No. 371572), larger than those above described.   From the same spot a detached abdomen of a *Callianassa* which appears to belong to this species (Cat. No. 371573).   On the third and the fourth segments are clusters of minute punctae suggestive of those patches either side of the palm.   The basal portion of the telson shows some shallow sculpturing, whereas the remainder has five deep longitudinal furrows.

Collection: U. S. National Museum; type, Cat. No. 371572.

Callianassa beta Rathbun, n.sp.

(Plate 15, figures 11-14)

Based on the distal portion of a left manus and its attached stump of a finger.   Upper and lower margins of palm nearly parallel, converging slightly at distal end.   Outer surface convex, inner surface slightly so except near the fixed finger, where it is concave.   Outer surface continuous with upper surface, ending in a blunt carina which flattens out at distal end. Lower margin lacking.   Finger broad, bent strongly inward; prehensile surface broad, deeply concave, both margins carinated; the inner carina has a sharp edge toward the concave surface; the outer carina is less prominent and has a row of ten minute punctae above.

Measurements: Holotype, height of manus, 8.7 millimeters; thickness of same, 4 millimeters; height of fixed finger at base, 3.2 millimeters; width at same point, 2.6 millimeters.

The broad, deeply excavated finger is the most distinguishing feature.

Occurrence: Alabama: Pine Barren section, Wilcox County; Sucarnoochee, Midway, lower Eocene; L. C. Johnson, collector (284); one specimen, holotype.

Collection: U. S. National Museum; type, Cat. No. 371507.

Callianassa gamma Rathbun, n.sp.

(Plate 17, figures 7-10)

A left manus, highest in the middle, tapering slightly at either end, thickest in its lowest half, one and a half times as long as high.   A straight, sharp carina above, directed inward.   An oblique, sinuous carina below, which at the thin finger end is at the middle of the lower surface but bends gradually over to the inner side of the lower surface, giving the article a twisted appearance.   The result is that neither carina is visible in an outer view, but the inner surface is bordered by them.   On the outer surface there is a deep furrow between the small finger end and the dactylar opening; opposite on the inner surface there is a blunt smooth ridge. Finger somewhat triangular in cross-section, broad above at the prehensile surface, pointed below. A longitudinal row of coarse punctae where outer and lower surfaces meet.

Measurements: Holotype, length of manus, 10 millimeters; height of same, 6.5 millimeters; greatest thickness, 3.6 millimeters.

Occurrence: Alabama: Prairie Creek, Wilcox County; Sucarnoochee beds, Midway, lower Eocene; L. C. Johnson, collector (Coll. No. 264); holotype.

Collection: U. S. National Museum; type, Cat. No. 371508.

Callianassa delta Rathbun, n.sp.
(Plate 15, figures 19–22)

A right palm and basal half of fixed finger. Palm three-quarters as high as long, outer surface vertically convex, upper margin a thin erect longitudinal carina. Below it on the inner side a row of eight, or more, oblique sockets, the distal five larger than the others. Inner surface for the most part convex, flattening toward the lower distal portion; a row of five distant punctae through the middle, a row of three along the upper third. Lower edge of palm and finger slightly sinuous, edge of palm thin, of finger less so, obscurely socketed, a row of five sockets just above the margin on the outer surface of the distal half of the palm. Finger narrow, inclined downward and inward, cross-section subcircular, prehensile margin thick, bordered on either side by a row of coarse, irregular granules which are continued back a little on the palm and border a short oblique furrow either side of the palm. The prehensile surface is oblique, higher outside than inside, and has a thick, blunt longitudinal ridge nearer the outer surface than the inner. The lower part of the margin of the dactylar cavity is granulate both inside and out; there is a row of three or four large flat sockets on the lower distal portion of the outer surface directed toward the finger.

Measurements: Holotype, length of palm at middle, 14 millimeters; greatest width, 9.8 millimeters; greatest thickness, toward proximal end, 4.6 millimeters; height of finger at base, 3 millimeters.

Occurrence: Alabama: Prairie Creek, Wilcox County; Sucarnoochee beds, Midway, lower Eocene; L. C. Johnson, collector (Coll. No. 264); holotype.

Collection: U. S. National Museum; type, Cat. No. 371509.

Callianassa epsilon Rathbun, n.sp.
(Plate 15, figures 15–18)

A left manus, proximal end incomplete, fingers lacking. Manus much higher at the distal than the proximal end, upper line oblique, nearly straight, lower margin arcuate. Upper margin broad and smoothly rounded; manus thick except toward the lower end where it is drawn to an acute edge, invisible in outer view and turned inward, and marked by a row of large punctae or sockets. Outer surface nearly smooth, a transverse line of punctae toward the proximal end, a groove of granules near the dactylus. Inner surface with large granules scattered on its lower two-thirds. The cross-section at the base of the immovable finger is subtriangular and occupies only one-third of the distal height of the manus.

The species differs from others associated with it by the greater distal height of the hand and the thick smoothly rounded upper border.

Measurements: Holotype, approximate length of manus, 11.8 millimeters; distal height, 10 millimeters; proximal height, 7.7 millimeters; greatest thickness, 5.2 millimeters.

Occurrence: Alabama: Prairie Creek region, Wilcox County; Sucarnoochee beds, Midway, lower Eocene; L. C. Johnson, collector (Coll. No. 264); holotype.

Collection: U. S. National Museum; type, Cat. No. 371510.

Callianassa alabamensis Rathbun, n.sp.

(Plate 15, figures 7-10)

Manus slightly longer through the middle than broad; in the holotype the proximal end is broken off. Outer surface a little more convex than lower, in a vertical direction. Upper margin arcuate, and lower margin also up to a point somewhat behind the base of finger; the margins gradually converge distally, both are slightly oblique to the proximal end; proximal angles broadly rounded. On the upper margin are 18 hair sockets which form as many parallel oblique lines on the inner surface; on the outside, close to the margin, a row of 15 punctae. On the lower margin, 21 sockets on the palm only and just outside a row of 11 distant punctae. On the distal third of the outer surface are a number of scattered punctae, which are continued on the base of the finger, where they tend to form linear vertical ridges. The fixed finger occupies at its base nearly half the height of the palm; it bends strongly inward, and has, so far as known, a straight horizontal lower edge on which are continued the markings of the palm; it is thick, broad-oval in cross-section, having a blunt carina on either side, parallel to the prehensile edge; a few punctae on each carina; on the prehensile edge (of the basal half or less) there are two teeth or lobes and proximal to the first one a row of five small tubercles. The movable finger has a straight upper margin for its basal two-thirds, then bends gradually downward; the upper margin is truncate; its principal carina, on the outer side is prominent, blunt and wavy; just below is a row of ten small punctae; the inner border of the flat upper surface is occupied by about 11 large oblique sockets; the prehensile edge has a large basal tooth followed by a row of about 15 small sockets; above this margin and on the outer surface are two irregular rows of punctae; about eight punctae are seen along the middle of the inner surface.

Measurements: Length (estimated) of right manus, holotype, 20.8 millimeters; width, 20.3 millimeters; thickness, 8.6 millimeters.

Occurrence: Alabama: Prairie Creek and Pine Barren section, Wilcox County; Sucarnoochee beds, Midway, lower Eocene; L. C. Johnson, collector (Coll. Nos. 264, 284); 20 specimens of manus, three of fingers, Cat. Nos. 371504, 371505 (including holotype).

Collection: U. S. National Museum; type, Cat. No. 371505.

Callianassa ulrichi C. A. White

(Plate 15, figures 1–3, 5, 6)

1880. *Callianassa ulrichi*. C. A. White, U. S. Nat. Mus., Pr., vol. 3, p. 161; vol. 4 (1881) p. 137, pl. 1, figs. 10 and 11; "Cretaceous."
1894. *Callianassa ulrichi*. G. D. Harris, Ark. Geol. Surv., Ann. Rept. for 1892, vol. 2, p. 36, pl. 1, fig. 2*a*, *b*; Midway, Eocene.
1925. *Callianassa ulrichi*. Rathbun, *in* Hull, Amer. Assoc. Pet. Geol., Bull., vol. 9, no. 1, p. 168.

Palm thick, convex outside, slightly convex inside except in the lower distal portion, which is flat or concave. Palm narrowing almost imperceptibly toward the distal end. Lower margin acutely carinate; just inside the carina there is a row of from 18 to 25 hair-sockets; in old worn specimens the sockets give the appearance of crenulation in outer view; above the carina on the outer surface a row of about six distant punctae. Upper margin more or less carinate until near the distal end; below the margin on the inner surface there are eight or nine, or more, fine punctae, the row bending downward at distal end. On outer surface there is between the fingers a broad triangular or subtruncate tooth with an acute tip at the lower end; its edge is granulate as also the corresponding edge of the inner surface. Outer surface with a cluster of flattened granules bordering the interdigital sinus. On the inner surface there is a nearly longitudinal band of coarse granules, running from the gap nearly the length of the palm. The fixed finger is long, gradually tapering, becoming very narrow; its lower edge is less acute than that of the palm and is furnished with punctae not quite so numerous as on the palm; the sockets just above the outer margin are continued along the finger. The prehensile edge has a row of large oblong punctae; a short ridge on the lower surface is granulate. Dactylus broader and thicker than fixed finger, prehensile edge wavy, subdentate; below the arcuate border there is a row of five punctae and toward the prehensile border on the same surface three or four punctae; outside there may be as many as six punctae along the prehensile border.

Measurements: Largest specimen (Mississippi), a right manus, length at middle, 14.2 millimeters; length at sinus, 11.7 millimeters; greatest width, 12.3 millimeters; least width, 11.6 millimeters. A similar smaller manus is proportionally longer.

Occurrence: Arkansas: Johnson's well, top of Capitol Hill, corner of Battery and 9th streets, Little Rock, Pulaski County; station 2218, Hayden Survey; Midway (Clayton limestone), lower Eocene; E. O. Ulrich, collector; 12 specimens of palms, with some fingers, cotypes, Cat. No. 8910; also, numerous specimens much worn and broken (261) Cat. No. 371585.

Arkansas: Buzzard Bluff on Red River, Section 16, Township 14 South, Range 26 West, Miller County; January, 1924; J. P. D. Hull, collector; Midway, lower Eocene; specimens returned to sender. Also, one specimen from the same place by the same collector, June 15, 1924; a right chela imbedded in dark shale, Cat. No. 371579.

Alabama: Prairie Creek, Wilcox County; Sucarnoochee beds, Midway, lower Eocene; 1883; L. C. Johnson. collector (264); one left palm, Cat. No. 371587.

Collections: U. S. National Museum, type, Cat. No. 8910; Hull collection.

Callianassa ulrichi claibornensis Rathbun, n.subsp.

(Plate 15, figure 4)

Differs as follows from typical *ulrichi*: Upper surface of manus carinate for little more than half its length, the distal end broadly rounded; on the inner surface just below the carina there is a row of eight or nine large punctae, which diverges distally from the middle line.

Occurrence:

Mississippi: East bank of the Chickasawhay River about half a mile below Enterprise, Clarke County; Claiborne, upper Eocene; October 23, 1912; E. N. Lowe and C. Wythe Cooke, collectors (6487); five palms, three loose propodal fingers.

Collection: U. S. National Museum, type, Cat. No. 371588.

Callianassa hulli Rathbun, n.sp.

(Plate 15, figures 30-35)

A small species, represented by a right manus, holotype, and impressions of several other palms. The lower margin almost at right angles to distal end, upper margin oblique to distal end, proximal margin oblique, forming an acute angle above and an obtuse angle below. Surfaces moderately convex, narrowing from the proximal to the distal end; above and below the palm is thin. The upper edge is sharp and narrow, and rough with numerous fine sockets; the proximal and the lower edges are marginate, and a little inside the margins there is on the outer surface a row of small spaced punctae. On the outer face a little behind the digital gap there is a group of more than 40 flattened and mostly oblong granules; from it a ridge runs obliquely down toward the immovable finger. On the lower half of the distal edge bordering the articulation with the dactyl there is a crowded row of granules. There are 12 sockets scattered on the outer surface: One below the middle of the upper margin; one, large near the distal end of the upper half; the others are on the lower half. The distal margin has a shallow blunt tooth above the middle of the articulation with the dactyl. On the inner surface there is, a little below the upper margin, a row of ten long linear coarse sockets which are at right angles to the margin; this is the most striking feature of the palm; above the lower margin, a row of numerous small round sockets, the interspaces as wide as sockets; a small bunch of granules opposite those on outer surface; middle of distal margin granulate; scattered sockets 21 or more, five of which are on the upper half.

A fragment of a finger shows three triangular, acute, prehensile teeth, separated by broad rounded sinuses. Another has a single tooth pointing distad. A proximal half of a left wrist has, above and parallel to its lower margin, a row of six round sockets, evenly spaced.

Measurements: Holotype, length of right manus, 7.4 millimeters; greatest width (proximal) of same, 6.3 millimeters; least width (distal), 5.5 millimeters approximately.

Occurrence: Found in small nodules, 11 millimeters or less in diameter. Arkansas: Buzzard Bluff, Miller County, Section 16, Township 14 South, Range 26 West; Midway, lower Eocene; J. P. D. Hull, collector.

Collection: U. S. National Museum; type, Cat. No. 371576.

Callianassa brazoensis Stenzel

1934. *Callianassa brazoensis.* Stenzel, Jour. Paleont., vol. 8, no. 1, p. 53, pl. 7, fig. 3*a–f.*

Manus characterized by four rows of socket pits, their number, and the shape of the manus, the proximal end of which slopes downward and inward.

Occurrence: Texas: Little Brazos River, Brazos County. Claiborne group, Cook Mountain formation, Crockett member.

Callianassa wechesensis Stenzel

1934. *Callianassa wechesensis.* Stenzel, Jour. Paleont., vol. 8, no. 1, p. 55, pl. 7, fig. 4*a, b.*

Differs from *C. brazoensis* by the nearly vertical and straight proximal end of palm, the shorter palm, and the group of tubercles near the interdigital sinus on the inner surface.

Occurrence: Texas: Leon County. Claiborne group, Mount Selman formation, Weches member.

Family PALINURIDAE
Genus LINUPARUS White
Linuparus texanus Rathbun, n.sp.

(Plate 16, figures 9, 10)

The abdomen of a single specimen, lacking the first and the second segments. Its length is one and two-thirds times the width at the third segment including the pleura. The third, fourth, fifth, and seventh segments are of subequal length on the median line; the sixth is a third longer. The third to sixth segments inclusive have each two median spines. The pleura of the third and fourth segments are rounded, the remainder are not exposed; the fourth pleuron is set off from the tergum by a smooth blunt ridge terminating in a stout conical spine pointing toward the carapace. A fragment of the outer layer on the penultimate segment is covered with large separated punctae. The telson is broader than long, arcuate at the extremity.

Measurements: Holotype, length of segments 3–7 of abdomen, 30.6

millimeters; width of fourth segment, measured along the surface, 23.8 millimeters.

Occurrence: Texas: Dimmit County; lower Midway; Julia A. Gardner, collector.

Collection: U. S. National Museum; type, Cat. No. 371390.

Linuparus wilcoxensis Rathbun, n.sp.
(Plate 16, figures 11–14)

Cervical suture deep. The after part of the dorsum of the carapace is bounded laterally by blunt parallel ridges, surface covered with granules of varying size, which are well separated except on the ridges, median and lateral, where they are crowded; on the median ridge some of the granules become spinulose with age. In front of the cervical suture the surface is more convex and the granulation finer and sparser; the sides are arcuate, the carapace being wider at the orbital angle than at the cervical suture; the outer margin is bluntly carinate; a second carina begins at the cervical suture almost in line with the lateral carina of the post-cervical section and curves forward and inward toward the anterior margin; two other carinae form an inverted V at the middle of the carapace; this V in the old separates into five tubercles with sharp points directed forward. Further forward are two pairs of similar tubercles, those of the anterior pair on the carapace margin a little nearer together than those of the posterior pair and forming the short frontal horns. The nearly vertical sides of the hinder part of the carapace are about one third as deep as long; its narrow anterior end is laterally swollen so as to be visible in dorsal view. The antero-lateral angle of the carapace terminates in a narrow spine directed forward and slightly outward. The epistome has an uneven surface, a median furrow not extending to the anterior margin, and separated on either side by a smooth and coarsely punctate elevation from a lateral depression; anterior margin with a forward-pointing tooth at either end.

The first article of the antennal peduncle is depressed, the lower surface bluntly angled at the inner third, the upper surface partially carinate at the outer third, the carina ending distally in a spine; the distal angles of the article are armed with a spine, and the outer margin has three short stout spinules; surface unevenly granulate and punctate.

Abdomen coarsely punctate especially on the median and lateral elevations. Segments 3–6 are of similar length. The pleura are, for the most part, incomplete; the second and third have each a spine at proximal end of lateral carina; the third has a slender spine at the middle of its outer margin and a tooth at posterior angle. There is one median spine on the first segment and two on segments 2, 3, and 4.

Measurements: Type, length of carapace (approximate), 47 millimeters; width at cervical suture, 23 millimeters. There are fragments of larger specimens, one having a carapace width of 34 millimeters and another, 39.4 millimeters approximately.

Relation: *L. canadensis*[37] differs from the new species in the after part of the carapace widening gradually behind, its three ridges spinous. In *L. vancouverensis*[38] the lateral ridges of the after part of the carapace curve gradually inward toward the cervical suture; the small ovate median area in front of the cervical suture is bordered by small tubercles.

Occurrence: Alabama:

Prairie Creek, Wilcox County, type locality; Sucarnoochee beds; about 20 fragments; L. C. Johnson, collector (Coll. No. 264). More numerous specimens are labeled "Prairie Creek and Pine Barren Section (Coll. No. 284)." One abdomen (Coll. No. 281). Cat. Nos. 371498–371500.

Estelle, Wilcox County: Sucarnoochee beds, Lower Eocene; one speciment (Ala. Mus. Nat. Hist.).

Black Bluff, Sumter County; one specimen loaned by E. W. Berry.

Collections: U. S. National Museum, type, Cat. No. 371499; Johns Hopkins University; Alabama Museum of Natural History.

Genus ARCHAEOCARABUS McCoy

Archaeocarabus (?) *gardnerae* Rathbun, n.sp.

(Plate 16, figures 19–21)

A portion of the hinder half of a carapace of a large specimen, and below it a left palm lacking extremities. Branchio-cardiac suture much depressed and nearly transverse at the middle, then curving gradually forward until it forms an obtuse angle and runs longitudinally forward and slightly downward; above this last portion there is for a distance a shallower groove subparallel to the other but somewhat sinuous and anteriorly converging toward it. From the branchio-cardiac suture at the right of the middle, a short, broad, shallow furrow runs obliquely backward and outward toward the posterior margin. The carapace is armed with large unequal, distant, conical spines whose tips are broken off. The surface between them is covered with small round pits largely of the socket type, trending backward, the anterior edge thickened and raised; sockets larger and more crowded on the forward part of the surface described; intervening space finely wrinkled.

The outer face of the palm is exposed. Upper and lower margins straight, gradually diverging distally. Lengthwise the surface is nearly level, but sideways convex; the upper fourth is set off by a row of ten large spines. The entire surface is rough with well separated socket-tubercles trending distad and more tubercular than those on the carapace. The upper margin shows several unequal spines, the stoutest at the distal end.

---

[37] *Podocratus canadensis* (Whiteaves). M. J. Rathbun: *The fossil stalk-eyed crustacea of the Pacific slope of North America*, U. S. Nat. Mus., Bull. 138 (1926) p. 134, pl. 35, fig. 2; pl. 36.

[38] *P. vancouverensis* (Whiteaves). *Op. cit.*, p. 135, pl. 37.

Measurements: Approximate length of post-cervical portion of carapace, 65 millimeters; approximate width of same, 60 millimeters; length of
palm, about 47 millimeters; greatest width of palm, 27 millimeters; proximal width, 20 millimeters.

Occurrence: Alabama: Black Bluff, Tombigbee River, Sumter County;
Midway, lower Eocene; 1929; Julia A. Gardner, collector; one specimen.

Collection: U. S. National Museum; type, Cat. No. 371515.

Family SCYLLARIDAE
Genus SCYLLARELLA Rathbun, n.gen.

Carapace broader than long, cardiac region strikingly prominent, cervical and branchio-cardiac grooves deep; a lateral carina extends from the
inner angle of the orbit to the posterior margin.

Genotype, *S. gibbera*, new species. *S. gardneri* (= *Scyllarides gardneri*
Woods[39]) and *Scyllarella mantelli* (= *Scyllarus mantelli* Desmarest[40]) may
also be placed in this genus.

Scyllarella gibbera Rathbun, n.sp.
(Plate 24, figures 35–40)

Two specimens showing carapace (incomplete) and sternum.   Carapace
broader than long (the anterior edge is lacking), and very convex from side
to side; it is separated into three parts by a furrow either side of the middle,
which terminates in a deep pit in front of posterior margin.   A remarkably
high prominence occupies the cardiac region; it has a gradual convex slope
behind, leading up from the posterior margin of the carapace; toward the
summit the edge is flat and covered by two rows of low tubercles; the
anterior slope of the prominence is steep and narrow above, but gradual
below, down to the cervical suture, widening into a triangular surface which
is sparsely covered with granules.   Gastric region with a similar but much
lower and smaller hump also trending forward, but with only one row of
tubercles on its posterior slope.   Opposite the highest point the cervical
suture turns abruptly outward to the lateral margin just behind the anterior angle.   Above the posterior margin and nearly meeting on the
medial line are two, low, triangular elevations somewhat granulate.   The
branchio-cardiac grooves have a row of tubercles continued forward a little
into the cervical suture, six or seven unequal tubercles in each; the lateral
carinae just outside the grooves converge slightly anteriorly before continuing to the inner margin of the orbit, and are rough with smaller separate tubercles.   The thin outer margin is curved up to the cervical groove
and is carinate, with nine, or more, low blunt teeth trending forward, one

[39] H. Woods: *A monograph of the fossil macrurous crustacea of England*, Palaeont. Soc. London, Mem., vol.
77 (1925) p. 39; vol. 78 (1926) pl. 10, fig. 6; Gault, England.

[40] A.-G. Desmarest *in* Brongniart and Desmarest; Histoire naturelle des crustacés fossiles (1822) p. 130;
Upper Cretaceous, England.

of which is in front of the cervical suture. Within the posterior half of this margin there are on the upper surface about 12 small tubercles most of which form a line parallel to the margin. The general surface of the carapace above and below is thickly covered with punctae.

Below and a little outside the lateral carina is the orbit. Sternum punctate, bordered by a row on each side of large round knobs at the insertion of the legs.

Measurements: Holotype, greatest width of carapace, 15.8 millimeters; width at articulation of abdomen, 8.1 millimeters; greatest height, 8 millimeters. The paratype is less well preserved but shows a little more of the anterior part of the carapace; greatest width behind cervical suture, 16.8 millimeters; width in front of cervical suture, (approximate) 15.5 millimeters.

Relation: Near *S. gardneri* (Woods), in which the carapace has more convex lateral margins with fewer spines or teeth and several spines instead of tubercles on the dorsum. *Scyllarus mantelli* Desmarest, which has never been figured, agrees with this species in having a carapace broader than long, a remarkable cardiac prominence, a smaller elevation that reaches nearly to the anterior border of the carapace, a deep excavation either side of the cardiac region, a deep furrow running from the antero-lateral angle to the median region. On the other hand, *S. mantelli* has a coarsely papillate instead of a punctate surface.

Occurrence: Alabama: Prairie Creek, Wilcox County; Sucarnoochee beds, Midway, lower Eocene; L. C. Johnson, collector; two carapaces (one is holotype), Cat. No. 371502, and one palm (Cat. No. 371501).

Collection: U. S. National Museum; type, Cat. No. 371502.

Scyllarella aspera Rathbun, n.sp.
(Plate 21, figure 18)

In the same region as *S. gibbera* was found a specimen showing the hinder half of the carapace (behind the cervical suture) and the first segment of the abdomen. The carapace is more than twice as wide as those of *gibbera*; the cardiac eminence is relatively just as prominent, but the upper part of the posterior slope is not so level as in *gibbera*. The prominence on either side of it, close to the margin of the carapace, is reduced to a tubercle; the tubercles forming the lateral carinae are unequal, two being much larger than the others. The depression between the median lobe and the lateral carina is deeper than in the genotype and devoid of a line of tubercles. A lateral carina is present on the abdominal segment and shows one much enlarged tubercle behind the middle; the center of the segment is broken but has an indication of a median prominence on the anterior third.

Occurrence: Alabama: Prairie Creek and Pine Barren section, Wilcox

County; Sucarnoochee beds, Midway, lower Eocene; L. C. Johnson, collector (284); one specimen.

Collection: U. S. National Museum; type, Cat. No. 371503.

Family PAGURIDAE
Genus PAGURISTES Dana
Paguristes johnsoni Rathbun, n.sp.

(Plate 14, figures 13–18)

One right major propodus of chela, one left minor chela.   Palm short and thick, quadrilateral in cross-section and with four blunt carinae as follows: One on inner margin marked off by a groove above and below, one on outer margin, one above, high to right of middle and leading obliquely outward and forward along the propodal finger, the fourth one below, near middle, oblique to outer margin, less oblique to inner margin.   Carinae coarsely and thickly granulate.   Viewed from above the outer margin is slightly convex, the inner margin more so.

A smaller left chela taken at a neighboring locality appears to be a minor chela of the same species.   The same carinae are present though less emphasized.   The fixed finger though broad at base becomes rapidly narrow and is longer than the palm.   A stump of the dactylus is narrower at base but as stout as the middle of the propodal finger.

Measurements: Holotype, major palm, length to base of finger, 15 millimeters; width, 12.6 millimeters; greatest thickness, 10 millimeters. Paratype, minor palm, width, 6.7 millimeters; greatest thickness, 5.3 millimeters; length of fixed finger, 7 millimeters; length of palm, uncertain.

Occurrence: Alabama: Wilcox County; Sucarnoochee beds, Midway, lower Eocene; L. C. Johnson, collector; Prairie Creek and Pine Barren section; holotype (284); Cat. No. 371705.   Prairie Creek; paratype (264); Cat. No. 371706.

Collection: U. S. National Museum; type, Cat. No. 371505.

Genus PAGURUS Fabricius
Pagurus alabamensis Rathbun, n.sp.

(Plate 16, figures 6–8)

Two right chelae.   Lateral margins arched upward.   Inner and outer margins of palm nearly straight, slightly arcuate outward; outer margin of fixed finger nearly straight, inclined a little outward but bending inward toward the tip.   Palm about as broad as long (proximal end broken off) and very thick especially in the middle of its width and in the distal half. Fixed finger broad at base, occupying three-fifths of width of palm, and tapering gradually toward end of finger (tip broken off).   Dactylus narrow, regularly tapering, concave on prehensile edge, convex outside.   The upper surface of the chela is rough with conical tubercles, mostly tipped with short stout spines and arranged largely in longitudinal rows. On the greater part of the outer half of this surface exclusive of the margin the tubercles are small and unarmed. On the lower surface there is next to each lateral margin a row of spines; also a row along the middle of the fixed finger and continued on the palm, composed of 12 or more tubercles. Outside this row are a few scattered tubercles, and more on the inner distal quarter; most of the surface is smooth and shining. The tubercles on the lower side of the dactylus are small, as also on the adjacent margin of the palm. Larger specimen similar but incomplete.

Measurements: Holotype, length of chela, 10.2 millimeters; width, 6 millimeters; greatest thickness, 4 millimeters; length of dactylus, 5.8 millimeters. Width of larger specimen, 8.8 millimeters.

Occurrence: Alabama: Prairie Creek, Wilcox County; Sucarnoochee beds, Midway; L. C. Johnson, collector (Coll. No. 264).

Collection: U. S. National Museum; type, Cat. No. 371703.

Family DROMIIDAE
Genus DROMILITES Milne Edwards
Dromilites americana Rathbun, n.sp.

(Plate 17, figures 1-6)

Carapace longer than broad, high in the middle, convex in both directions. The 12 bosses and all the protuberances of the thickened margin are rough with coarse, crowded granules; intermediate spaces smooth and finely punctate. The mesogastric boss is highest and is round, as are also the protogastric boss (paired) and the one at the inner angle of the branchial region, which is behind the line of the mesogastric boss. A tubercle on the hepatic region is much smaller than the other dorsal prominences. There are five transverse elevations, one on either side at the widest part of the carapace (which tends to be round in small specimens), one cardiac, and one branchial, on either side of the cardiac region and more or less horn-shaped, the thin end curving up the lateral margin of the carapace. A deep median furrow runs from the mesogastric region to the edge of the front; the anterior part of that region is linear. Front advanced, deflexed, bilobed, lobes oblique, separated by a U-shaped sinus and with concave margin, forming two small lobules. Two closed fissures in upper margin of orbit; outer tooth thick, triangular in dorsal view, and separated by a U-sinus from the blunt inner tooth of the lower margin. Three antero-lateral lobes, increasing in size from first to third, the third at the lateral angle of the carapace. The postero-lateral margin is about one and a half times as long as the antero-lateral; it is divided by a shallow sinus into two thickened lobes; the distance between the middle of these lobes is equal to the width of the front.

Lower surface of carapace and pterygostomian region partly granulate. Antennae and abdomen not preserved. Two detached chelipeds show the carpus, the manus, and part of the fixed finger. Surface finely punctate and partly granulate; a short oblique carina near articulation of carpus with manus; manus swollen in the middle both in dorsal and in lateral aspect; finger slender, bent strongly downward; cross-section of base of dactylus large.

Measurements: Holotype (284) extreme length of carapace, 18.4 millimeters; greatest width, 18.3 millimeters; fronto-orbital width, 8 millimeters; width of front at outer lobules, 4 millimeters. Another specimen from the same gathering, extreme length of carapace, 18.8 millimeters; greatest width, 17.3 millimeters; fronto-orbital width, 9 millimeters; width of front at outer lobules, 4 millimeters. The difference in the width of these two specimens may be due to sex.

Occurrence:

Alabama: Sucarnoochee beds: Prairie Creek and Pine Barren section, Wilcox County; L. C. Johnson, collector (Coll. No. 284); 32 carapaces (Cat. No. 371687).

Prairie Creek and Allenton, Wilcox County; L. C. Johnson, collector (Coll. No. 264); 18 carapaces including holotype, two chelipeds (Cat. No. 371688).

Pine Barren Creek, Wilcox County; L. C. Johnson, collector (Coll. Nos. 7–11); one specimen (Ala. Mus. Nat. Hist.).

Black Bluff, Tombigbee River, Sumter County; Julia Gardner, collector, three carapaces (Cat. No. 371698); E. A. Smith, collector; July 20, 1886, one specimen (Ala. Mus. Nat. Hist.).

Texas: Milam County: Wise No. 1 well, depth 785 feet, distance above base of formation, 130 feet; John E. Adams, California Oil Company, collector; one carapace.

Collections: U. S. National Museum, type, Cat. No. 371688; Alabama Museum of Natural History; California Oil Company.

Family LEUCOSIIDAE
Genus HEPATISCUS Bittner
Hepatiscus americanus Rathbun, n.sp.

(Plate 17, figure 11)

Anterior three-fifths of a carapace. Surface finely punctate in the depression between the gastric and the branchio-hepatic regions; closely granulate elsewhere especially on the conical elevations, six of which are of large size: two protogastric, one mesogastric, two epibranchial, one cardiac; in the depression either side of the cardiac elevation there is a small low cone. Lateral margin thick, slightly ascending; the anterior part is arcuate, the lateral borders subparallel, moderately curved. Orbits finely edged, directed forward. Interorbital front lacking.

Measurements: Width of carapace, 11.6 millimeters; fronto-orbital width, 5.8 millimeters; width of orbit, 1.7 millimeters.

Relation: In the arrangement of the tubercles, this species resembles *H. pulchellus* Bittner[41] from the Lutetian of the Venetian Alps, but is more squarely built and the fronto-orbital width greater.

Occurrence: Alabama: Prairie Creek, Wilcox County; Sucarnoochee beds, Midway, lower Eocene; L. C. Johnson, collector (264); one specimen.

Collection: U. S. National Museum; type, Cat. No. 371695.

Family RANINIDAE
Genus RANINOIDES Milne Edwards
Raninoides ovalis Rathbun, n.sp.

(Plate 18, figures 1-8)

Carapace suboval, about one and a half times as long as broad, fronto-orbital distance about equal to posterior margin; surface smoothly rounded from side to side and from back to front except for a short space behind the front margin, which is almost imperceptibly depressed nearly as far as the blunt and insignificant lateral tooth. Surface closely punctate and with larger scattered punctae; around the front and the antero-lateral margins, coarsely granulate; two crescentic lines in middle of carapace. Postero-lateral margin a raised line of granules set off by a groove; posterior margin nearly straight, corners rounded. No specimen has the anterior margin entire. The orbital fissures are open in the shape of a narrow V; the outer tooth is obliquely truncate, the next tooth transversely so; the space between the two innermost fissures is advanced only in the middle half where there is a shallow rounded lobe which may have had a pointed tip (fig. 5). This specimen has a smooth swelling on the right side of the carapace, indicative of an internal parasite. The pterygostomian region and the sternum are coarsely granulate; the chelipedal sternum bears a large swelling at its middle; the two following sections are thickened along the outer side and deeply furrowed in the middle. Of the abdominal segments, the first is narrower (from right to left) than the second, ends concave; the second has arcuate ends, the third is narrower; surface finely granulate.

A detached right palm (264) appears to belong here; it resembles a fragment of one which is attached to a carapace. Palm short and thick, surface covered with fine unequal, separated granules, coarser on the outer surface than elsewhere. Upper margin arcuate in profile, a proximal lobe above attachment of carpus; inner surface with a short, longitudinal furrow below upper margin; a corresponding, but shallower, depression on outer surface; distal end broken off near articulation with dactylus. The basal

---

[41] A. Bittner: *Die brachyuren des Vicentinischen Tertiärgebirges*, Denkschr. Akad. d. Wissensch., Wien, vol. 34 (1875) p. 75 [15] pl. 1, figs. 9 and 10.

portion of fixed finger indicates an almost vertical direction; a longitudinal linear carina on distal side.

Measurements: Largest specimen, length, about 27.2 millimeters; width, 20 millimeters.   Length of a detached palm, 5.5 millimeters; height, 4.2 millimeters; thickness, 3.2 millimeters; height of dactylar opening, 2 millimeters; width of base of fixed finger, 0.9 millimeter.

Occurrence: Alabama; Sucarnoochee beds; L. C. Johnson, collector:

Prairie Creek and Allenton, Wilcox County (264); 32 carapaces (incomplete) and one wrist, Cat. Nos. 371501 and 371689.

Prairie Creek and Pine Barren section, Wilcox County (284); three specimens, Cat. No. 371692.

Collection: U. S. National Museum; type, Cat. No. 371689.

Genus NOTOSCELES Bourne
Notosceles bournei Rathbun

(Plate 16, figure 16; Plate 26, figure 5)

1928. *Notosceles bournei*.   Rathbun, U. S. Nat. Mus., Pr., vol. 73, art. 6, p. 1, pl. 1.

Occurrence:
Arkansas: Buzzard Bluff, Section 16, Township 14 South, Range 26 West, Miller County; Midway; J. P. D. Hull, collector; two specimens, returned.
Texas: Navarro County, Thomas Jordan Survey, in core drill, Lane No. 1, depth 260 feet; Marland Oil Company; holotype, Cat. No. 369608.
Texas: Navarro County, near Kerens; Midway; D. W. Ohern, Borealis Oil Company, collector; one specimen, Cat. No. 371525.
Alabama: Prairie Creek and Allenton, Wilcox County; Sucarnoochee beds; L. C. Johnson, collector (264); one specimen consisting of three-fifths of a carapace with sternum attached, and another larger specimen showing the hinder half of the carapace and the left lateral spine; Cat. No. 371702.
Alabama: Black Bluff, Tombigbee River, Sumter County; Sucarnoochee beds: station 12032; 1929; Julia Gardner, collector; parts of three specimens, two of which show the sternum; Cat. No. 371696.   From the same locality, one specimen collected by E. A. Smith, July 20, 1886.
Collections: U. S. National Museum, type, Cat. No. 369608; Hull collection, and Alabama Museum of Natural History.

Remarks: The pterygostomial suture runs near the postero-lateral margin of the carapace, especially at the widest part and gradually diverges from it posteriorly. The eleventh and twelfth sternal segments are each provided with a stout, granulated, marginal tooth overlapping the carapace.

Genus RANINELLA A. Milne Edwards
Raninella eocenica Rathbun, n.sp.

(Plate 18, figures 13–16)

Carapace about one and a third times as long as broad, convex from side to side, slightly so from back to frontal region which is horizontal or slightly ascending; carapace widest a little behind the middle; posterior margin slightly concave and nearly as long as the fronto-orbital distance. Surface closely punctate; granulate near the antero-lateral margin; a deep thumb-nail impression either side of the median line behind the middle of the carapace.   Postero-lateral margin rimmed; antero-lateral thick, armed with two spines twice as far apart as the anterior spine is from the orbital spine; the posterior spine is directed outward, the next one obliquely forward. At outer end of orbit a long, cylindrical spine directed forward, and close to it a tapering spine, then a notch; the front appears to be tridentate; all spines are incomplete. In front view the anterior edge of the carapace is strongly arched. The lower surface of the carapace is coarsely granulate, as are also the merus and the carpus of the cheliped. Sternum not known.

Occurrence: Alabama; Sucarnoochee beds:

Prairie Creek, Wilcox County; L. C. Johnson, collector (Coll. No. 264); four specimens, including type, and also a spine-bearing fragment, Cat. No. 371701.

Prairie Creek and Pine Barren section, Wilcox County; L. C. Johnson, collector (Coll. No. 284); three specimens, Cat. No. 371700.

Collection: U. S. National Museum; type, Cat. No. 371701.

Genus SYMETHIS Weber

1795. *Symethis.*   Weber, Nomenclator entomologicus, p. 92.
1798. *Symethis.*   Fabricius, Suppl. Entom. Syst., p. 371.
1888. *Zanclifer.*   Henderson, *Challenger* Rept., Zool., vol. 27, p. 34.

Symethis johnsoni Rathbun, n.sp.
(Plate 17, figures 12–17)

Carapace urn-shaped, having a large hepatic marginal spine directed obliquely forward and outward, in front of which the carapace narrows abruptly, and with subparallel or slightly diverging sides to the line of the orbits. A slender spine at outer angle of orbit. Between the orbits the carapace again abruptly narrows, forming a quadrate, subtruncate, bilobed rostrum. Carapace a little constricted behind the hepatic spine, then widening to a point in front of the middle, thence it narrows in a sinuous line to the slightly concave posterior margin. This margin is half as wide as the fronto-orbital distance. Surface closely covered with large punctae, becoming smaller on the anterior fourth or fifth; a blunt median ridge begins narrow at the posterior margin and gradually widens and disappears anteriorly; a short and narrow intermediate ridge runs obliquely forward from the posterior margin and parallel to the lateral margin. Lateral margin thick and granulate. Orbits large, nearly transverse.

Ischium of outer maxillipeds long and narrow, increasing in width a little from the proximal to the distal end; merus seemingly about half as long. Pterygostomian regions much swollen, granulated. Sternum between chelipeds of characteristic Raninid shape; the next segment is extended widely between cheliped and first leg; following segment relatively narrow, produced little laterally, the bases of the first and second legs being close together. Abdomen narrow; first segment with oblique side margins; second much longer, increasing in width distally, lateral margins sinuous; third segment about two-thirds as long as the preceding.

Measurements: Holotype (371705), length of carapace to line of orbits, 23.2 millimeters; greatest width behind hepatic spine, 14.4 millimeters; fronto-orbital width, 8.4 millimeters; posterior width, 4.6 millimeters.

Remarks: Resembles the Recent *S. caribensis* in the front advanced abruptly beyond the orbits, and in the general arrangement of the sternal segments.

Occurrence: Alabama: Sucarnoochee beds, Midway:

Prairie Creek and Allenton, Wilcox County; L. C. Johnson, collector (264); 19 specimens, Cat. No. 371693; one holotype, Cat. No. 371705.

Prairie Creek and Pine Barren section, Wilcox County; L. C. Johnson, collector (284); 20 specimens, Cat. No. 371691.

Black Bluff, Sumter County; E. A. Smith, collector; July 20, 1886; two fragments (Ala. Mus. Nat. Hist.).

Collections: U. S. National Museum, type, Cat. No. 371705; Alabama Museum of Natural History.

Genus SYMNISTA Philippi
Symnista bidentata Rathbun, n.sp.
(Plate 18, figures 9-12)

Represented by a single small and incomplete specimen which is placed in this genus because of its long, egg-shaped body, narrow front, and prominent antero-lateral protuberance.

The specimen consists of perhaps two-thirds of a carapace with a large part of the right margin and a small part of the left margin, a cross-section of an orbit, and a large part of the pterygostomian regions. The cross-section of the carapace behind its middle is a broad oval. Near the hinder end of the fragment there is on the dorsal surface a pair of parallel impressions, indicating the position of gastro-cardiac area; if this surmise is correct, the entire length of the carapace would be unusually great compared to its width. The antero-lateral margin bears two teeth, subtriangular, depressed, the hinder one large and with a long posterior slope, the anterior one small. In front of these teeth the margin turns forward and slightly outward, and extends farther forward than the distance between the teeth. The anterior broken edge shows the cross-section of the orbit which is so large that it indicates a narrow space remaining for the front. Surface above and below closely punctate, the fine punctae having a scattering of larger ones; the lateral margin is thick and blunt. Buccal cavity long in proportion to its width.

Measurements: Holotype, width behind larger lateral spine, 7.6 millimeters; thickness at same level (measured through pterygostomian region), 4.2 millimeters; fronto-orbital width, (estimated) 6 millimeters; width of orbit, 1.6 millimeters.

Occurrence: Alabama: Prairie Creek and Allenton, Wilcox County; Sucarnoochee beds; L. C. Johnson, collector (Coll. No. 264); one specimen. Collection: U. S. National Museum; type, Cat. No. 371742.

Family CALAPPIDAE
Genus CALAPPILIA A. Milne Edwards
Calappilia diglypta Stenzel

1934. *Calappilia diglypta.* Stenzel, Jour. Paleont., vol. 8, no. 1, p. 51, pl. 7, fig. 2a, b. Differs from allied species in the much smaller number of its carapace tubercles.

Occurrence: Texas: Stone City, Burleson County. Claiborne group, Cook Mountain formation, Crockett member.

Family XANTHIDAE
Genus MENIPPE DeHaan
Menippe burnsi Rathbun, n.sp.
(Plate 19, figures 1-11)

Represented by three right major palms, two left minor palms, two left minor palms, and one right wrist with a fragment of the palm attached. Palms massive, almost as convex inside as outside, thickest at the middle. A furrow along the proximal end, inside and out. Outer layer covered with fine but separated granules and more distant punctae. The articulating condyle on the outside adjacent to the dactylus is somewhat elongate heartshaped, similar to the same lobe in Recent *Menippe*, and is set off by a deep groove. The major palm is much higher at the distal than at the proximal end; lower margin nearly straight, forming an acute angle with the distal margin; proximal end oblique. The minor palm has the upper and the lower surfaces more nearly parallel, the upper slightly arcuate and separated by a deep furrow from the prominent condyle at the proximal end; the palm is highest at the distal end, lowest at the proximal end. The stump of the fixed finger of the minor chela is slightly deflexed; the cross-section of the base occupies about a third of the height of the manus. The base of the dactylus appears to meet or nearly meet that of the propodal finger. The carpus of a right cheliped is a little longer, measured on the inner margin, than its greatest width; the tooth at inner angle is small, conical, and blunt. The proximal end of the lower margin of the attached palm is slightly concave, but whether it belongs to a major or a minor cheliped is undetermined.

One of the right palms is of relatively small size and is placed here with some reservation; the upper-outer surface is covered with coarse, separated granules, which do not perhaps represent the outer layer. None of the larger and more worn palms shows this granulation.

Measurements: Holotype, left palm, length of upper margin, 45 millimeters; length at middle, 53.6 millimeters; height at middle, 39.7 millimeters, distal height, (estimated) 41.3 millimeters; greatest thickness, 26.7 millimeters.

Additional material: A single dactylus or movable finger of the right cheliped is referred to this species. The granulation agrees with that on the stump of a finger attached to the holotype palm; the granules are unequal, separated at irregular intervals. The finger is thick throughout its height and length, tapers to a broad blunt tip, and curves inward almost imperceptibly. On both inner and outer surfaces there is a shallow longitudinal depression through the middle, which follows the curve of the finger and is broad at the proximal end and gradually diminishes, fading out midway of the length of the finger. There are also two inconspicuous rows of distant punctae on either side, but without the impressed groove common in the Recent *Menippe* just below the upper surface, inside and out. The prehensile edge shows traces of four or five low teeth.

Occurrence:

North Carolina: City quarry near cemetery, Wilmington, New Hanover County; Castle Hayne marl, Jackson formation, upper Eocene; 1902; Frank Burns, collector (3602); type lot; Cat. No. 371580.

South Carolina: Belle Broughton plantation, half a mile southeast of Creston, Calhoun County, on branch of Halfway Swamp; Santee limestone, basal Jackson formation, upper Eocene; 1917; C. W. Cooke, collector (Coll. No. 7990); one finger, Cat. No. 371581.

Collection: U. S. National Museum; type, Cat. No. 371580.

Menippe jakcsonensis Rathbun, n.sp.
(Plate 19, figure 16)

Portion of a right minor chela, showing the inner surface of both fingers and the distal end of the palm. Distal margin of palm oblique so that the fixed finger is shorter than the dactylus. Both fingers are dark colored, almost black, the color reaching nearly to the base of the dactylus and occupying two-thirds, or more, of the immovable finger and ending proximally in a concave line; it is probable that the color runs farther back on the outer surface. Both fingers are bluntly pointed. The dactylus is narrow, subcylindrical, regularly tapering, and curved, and falls short of the tip of the dactyl when flexed; a line of punctae runs longitudinally below the middle; no prehensile teeth are evident. The immovable finger is elongate-triangular, with a sinuous lower margin, three broad, low teeth on prehensile edge, tip upturned; a row of punctae at lower third, subparallel to lower margin.

This species has a more slender dactyl than any of the Recent species in the Caribbean area, but approaches that of *M. obtusa*,[42] in which, however, the propodal finger is longer and dark-colored throughout.

[42] M. J. Rathbun: *The cancroid crabs of America of the families Euryalidae, Portunidae, Atelecyclidae, Cancridae, and Xanthidae*, U. S. Nat. Mus., Bull. 152 (1930) pl. 198, fig. 1.

Measurements: Length of dactylus, 10.7 millimeters; of fixed finger, upper margin, 6.5 millimeters.

Occurrence: Mississippi: Bluff on the west side of Town Creek, Jackson, 200 feet south of Rankin Street and 800± feet west of South State Street; Jackson formation, upper Eocene; October 9, 1912; C. Wythe Cooke, collector (6465); holotype.

Collection: U. S. National Museum; type, Cat. No. 371589.

Menippe anomala Rathbun, n.sp.

(Plate 19, figures 12-15)

A portion of a right manus, the extremities lacking. Manus high, thick; outer surface very convex in a vertical direction, less convex longitudinally; upper surface continuous with the outer, longitudinally arched and covered with large separated granules, which are continued for a slight distance on the outer surface, more so at the proximal end than toward the dactyl; inner surface smooth and punctate, flat in the upper portion and along the lower border, but with a large swelling covering the middle portion of the proximal half of the manus; lower margin blunt—only a small part of it remains—and trending downward from the proximal end. The customary nodule above the articulation with the carpus is broken off; a short interspace exists between it and the carpus.

The arcuate upper margin, combined with the abruptly flattened inner surface, distinguishes this species from others.

Occurrence: North Carolina: City quarry near cemetery, Wilmington, New Hanover County; Castle Hayne marl, Jackson formation, upper Eocene; 1902; Frank Burns, collector (Coll. No. 3602).

Collection: U. S. National Museum; type, Cat. No. 371524.

Genus OCALINA Rathbun
Ocalina floridana Rathbun

1929. *Ocalina floridana.* Rathbun, U. S. Nat. Mus., Pr., vol. 75, art. 15, p. 2, pls. 1–3.

Occurrence: Florida: Alachua, Levy, and Marion counties. Ocala limestone, upper Eocene.
Collection: U. S. National Museum; type, Cat. No. 370956.

Genus HARPACTOCARCINUS A. Milne Edwards
Harpactocarcinus americanus Rathbun

1928. *Harpactocarcinus americanus.* Rathbun, U. S. Nat. Mus., Pr., vol. 73, art. 6, p. 3, pls. 2 and 3.
1929. *Xanthopsis americana.* Glaessner, Fossilium Catalogus, 1, pars 41, p. 395.

Type-locality: Texas: Little Brazos Creek, Brazos County, on both sides of the old Bryan and Brazos Valley Railroad bridge; holotype, Cat. No. 369607.
Additional localities:
Texas: San Augustine, San Augustine County; lower fossiliferous bed; November 28, 1908; T. W. Vaughan, collector (5119); one specimen, Cat. No. 371582.

Texas: Northeast of Moseley's Ferry, northwestern Brazos County; Cook Mountain formation of the lower Claiborne of the horizon of the Moseley Ferry beds, upper Eocene; John Vick, collector; four specimens, Cat. No. 371578.

Texas: Dunn ranch, Brazos County; Cook Mountain formation; 1930; P. H. McCauley, W. S. Adkins, collectors.

Louisiana: Half a mile north of Natchitoches Parish; Wahtubbee, lower Claiborne, Eocene; 1894; T. W. Vaughan, collector (2912); one female, Cat. No. 147438.

Mississippi: Wahtubbee Hills, cut on New Orleans and Northeastern Railway, 4 miles south of Enterprise, Clark County; lower Claiborne; 1894; Frank Burns, collector; one major claw of male; Cat. No. 371584.

Collections: U. S. National Museum, type, Cat. No. 369607; University of Texas.

Harpactocarcinus rathbunae Stenzel

1934. *Harpactocarcinus rathbunae.* Stenzel, Jour. Paleont., vol. 8, no. 1, p. 46, pl. 6, fig. 2a, b.

Differs from *H. americanus* in its greater size and in the lower margin of the right manus very sinuous.[43]

Occurrence: Texas: Little Brazos River, Brazos County. Claiborne group, Cook Mountain formation, Crockett member.

Harpactocarcinus sp. Stenzel

1934. *Harpactocarcinus,* sp. Stenzel, Jour. Paleont., vol. 8, no. 1, p. 46, pl. 6, fig. 3.

This species has a form of chela intermediate between those of the two preceding species.

Occurrence: Texas: Little Brazos River, Brazos County. Claiborne group, Cook Mountain formation, Crockett member.

Harpactocarcinus mississippiensis Rathbun, n.sp.

(Plate 21, figures 9–11)

In the female specimen at hand, the carapace is badly cracked and the margins for the most part broken away. Carapace subcircular, broader than long; convex from side to side and much more so from front to back, the anterior and the posterior margins invisible in dorsal view; surface covered with fine punctae irregular in shape and size; marginal teeth unknown. Orbits far apart, subcircular, upper margin thickened, tubular. Front between the orbits triangular, nearly three times as broad as long.

Chelipeds massive, unequal, the right the larger. Outer surface of merus broader than long, outer surface of carpus much longer than broad. Outer surface of manus convex from upper to lower edge, irregularly pitted and bearing four longitudinal rows of small tubercles, one on the upper margin, the second near it but diverging a little distally; two rows further apart at middle of manus and composed of somewhat smaller tubercles. These disappear on the distal part of the major manus. The number of tubercles in the various rows, beginning at the top, are as follows: Minor palm, 7, 7, 8+, 5+; major palm 4+, 8, 7, 4. In the space be-

---

[43] I am not convinced that *H. rathbunae* is distinct from *americanus.* The chelae of the latter vary with age, the lower margin in the younger nearly horizontal, but in the older gradually bending downward except at the tip.

tween the second and the third rows of the major palm are two groups of tubercles at either end, four in the proximal group and five in the distal; breaks in the shell have destroyed all but two tubercles in the proximal group of the minor palm. A shallow punctate groove on the fixed finger is continued a ways on the palm. Fingers stout, tips blunt; fixed finger nearly horizontal, convex below, prehensile margin slightly sinuous, in the main convex; dactylus slightly curved, inner margins nearly straight, unarmed. Merus of ambulatory legs broad, compressed.

Of the female abdominal segments, the first is broad, the second much narrower, the third nearly as broad as the first, the fourth, fifth, and sixth a little broader and subequal to one another in width. As to length (in the direction of the axis of the animal), the first segment is short in the middle, longer at the ends; the second, third, and fourth are a little longer and subequal to one another, the fifth is a little longer, the sixth is fully twice as long as the fifth, the seventh is concealed.

Measurements: Holotype, female, length of carapace, 71 millimeters; estimated minimum width of same, 81.5 millimeters; fronto-orbital width, 44.5 millimeters; interorbital width, 34.5 millimeters; length of propodus of major chela, 40.2 millimeters; height of same, 25.3 millimeters; length of propodus of minor chela, 36 millimeters; height of same, 21.6 millimeters.

Relation: Approaches *H. rotundatus* A. Milne Edwards[44] from the nummulitic terrain of Verona, in proportions of carapace and the double row of tubercles on the upper part of the palm. In our species the middle of the front is more advanced, and the palm is tuberculated through the middle. The surface of the carapace is suggestive of *H. punctulatus* (Desmarest) figured by that author;[45] the abdomen is similar to that of the same species.[46]

Occurrence: Jackson formation, upper Eocene:

Mississippi: Large ravine below old reservoir at Yazoo City, about one mile south of the Yazoo and Mississippi Valley Railroad station, along street-car line; October 11, 1912; E. N. Lowe and C. W. Cooke, collectors (6472); one female, holotype; Cat. No. 371577.

Alabama: Choctaw County, N. H. Boss and A. R. Kellogg, collectors, 1929: Old Sanford Mitchell field about 2 miles southeast of Melvin, Section 24, Township 11 North, Range 5 West, October 12, one right chela; 2.4 miles by road south of Melvin, southeast quarter of Section 26, Township 11 North, Range 5 West, October 22, one right chela.

Collection: U. S. National Museum; type, Cat. No. 371577.

[44] A. Milne Edwards: *Monographie des crustacés fossiles de la famille des cancériens*, Ann. Sci. Nat., Paris, Zool., ser. 4, vol. 18 (1862) p. 71, pl. 10, figs. 2-2d.

[45] A.-G. Desmarest *in* Brongniart [and Desmarest: *Histoire naturelle des crustacés fossiles*, Paris (1822) pl. 7, fig. 3.

[46] *Op. cit.*, pl. 7, fig. 4.

Genus ZANTHOPSIS M'Coy
Zanthopsis errans Woods
(Plate 21, figures 15–17)

1922. *Xanthopsis errans.* Woods, *in* Bosworth, Geol. N. W. Peru, p. 115, pl. 17, figs. 7–10; Clavilithes series, Negritos formation.

This much worn specimen shows the essential characters of the species: Four tubercles on the outer surface of the palm, two rows of tubercles on the curved upper surface, a slender propodal finger, and the stump of a mammoth dactyl. The socket of the dactyl is at least as wide and as high as the cross-section of the base of the fixed finger.

Occurrence: Mississippi: Clark County; Wahtubbee horizon, lower Claiborne, middle Eocene; Frank Burns, collector; one right chela, Cat. No. 139148.

Collections: U. S. National Museum; Sedgwick Museum, Cambridge, type.

Zanthopsis carolinensis Rathbun, n.sp.
(Plate 20, figures 1, 2)

A male showing the greater part of the carapace (margin excepted), the sternum, and the abdomen. Carapace about six-sevenths as long as broad, convex in all directions especially antero-posteriorly. Surface not very uneven, a narrow shallow depression begins at the margin of the front, widens backward, merging with the mesogastric region. Either side of the middle, a broad deep longitudinal furrow bounds the metagastric to the intestinal region and anteriorly turns outward toward the hepatic region. A narrow furrow borders the posterior margin. The following smoothly rounded elevations are noted: One large and low on each protogastric region; one large and high at the inner angle of the branchial region; one smaller, a little farther outward and forward; one high in transverse line with cardiac region; and one lower in the same line but farther out. In the furrows alongside the urogastric-cardiac connection there are two linear crescentic granulated elevations. Two granules side by side at the meta-gastric region, two farther apart on the cardiac region, and one median on the intestinal or postcardiac region. Front narrow, four-lobed.

Sternum narrow, anterior end in front of chelipeds deeply recessive. At the articulation with the chelipeds there is a large prominent oblong tubercle. The lateral lobes of the coalesced (third to fifth) segment of the abdomen are prominent; the segment is not much longer than its anterior or distal width. The penultimate segment gradually diminishes; its length is two-thirds of its proximal width. Terminal segment subtriangular.

Measurements: Male holotype, length of carapace, 61.2 millimeters; width of same, 70 millimeters; width of front, 15 millimeters; of orbit, 6 millimeters.

Occurrence: South Carolina: Creston, Orangeburg County; lower Claiborne, middle Eocene; T. W. Vaughan, collector (4585).

Collection: U. S. National Museum; type, Cat. No. 371586.

Zanthopsis peytoni Stenzel

1934. *Zanthopsis peytoni*. Stenzel, Jour. Paleont., vol. 8, no. 1, p. 49, pl. 7, fig. 1*a–c*.
Differs from all other species of the genus by the pair of spines on the posterior margin. The bosses of the protogastric region are quite conspicuous though low; the branchial regions carry five bosses.

Occurrence: Texas: Several places in Leon County. Claiborne group, Mount Selman formation, Weches member, bed *d*.

Zanthopsis peytoni var. *parva* Stenzel

1934. *Zanthopsis peytoni* var. *parva*. Stenzel, Jour. Paleont., vol. 8, no. 1, p. 51.
Smaller than the specific form.

Occurrence: Texas: Several places in Leon County. Claiborne group, Mount Selman formation, Weches member, bed *g*.

Genus XANTHILITES Bell
Xanthilites alabamensis Rathbun, n.sp.
(Plate 20, figures 3–16)

Carapace hexagonal, antero-lateral shorter than postero-lateral margin, and cut into four strong triangular teeth. Of these, the first or orbital tooth points forward, the second and third obliquely forward and outward, the third the wider, whereas the fourth, the largest of all, is directed outward and slightly upward. Front divided into two oblique lobes, each of which is divided into two smaller lobules; the interspaces are U-shaped, the median narrower than the lateral. Sides of front, at base of eyestalks, concave. Upper margin of orbit transverse; width of orbit from tip to tip a little less than width of front; in the upper margin, two obscure notches indicated by short closed fissures and not interrupting the general direction of the margin. In front view the orbits appear oblong and slope obliquely downward outwardly; the front is deflected to a point a little below the middle of the orbit. The general surface of the carapace is rough with fine scabrous granules, but the elevated portions—the 12 bosses, the antero-lateral teeth, the thickened parts of the fronto-orbital margin—are covered with coarse granules. The median regions, gastric and cardiac, are separated on either side by a deep furrow from the branchio-hepatic regions; in this furrow opposite the shallow gastro-cardiac depression there is a deep thumbnail impression. Shallow grooves define the protogastric from the mesogastric region and the hepatic from the orbital and branchial regions. The bosses are distributed as follows: one protogastric (paired), one mesogastric, covering the greater part of the region, one cardiac, one hepatic, the smallest of all, three branchial; of these, one is in a transverse line with the lateral tooth and the mesogastric boss, another is at the inner angle of the region and a little behind the transverse line; the third is subconical, above the postero-lateral margin and directed outward and upward.

Orbits deep; a prominent tooth at inner angle of lower border, broadly rounded and nearly as advanced as the outer lobule of the front, its outer slope forming with the outer tooth of the orbit a broad and deep V-shaped notch, its inner slope bordered in the hinder part by a small, conical tooth, mostly hidden in ventral view.   Pterygostomian region finely granulate. Basal segment of antennules subtriangular, large, exposed surface uneven and partly granulate, oblique outer margin in front view in line with outer margin of outer lobule of front.   Basal segment of antennae small, wedged in the orbital hiatus.   A strong endostomial crest present.   Epistome deeply notched outside the crest and with a median buttonhole notch. Anterior part of sternum uneven, elevations granulated; female abdomen of moderate width, male abdomen not known.

Chelipeds stout; merus nearly as broad as long on the outer surface, lower margin thick; carpus much broader than long, the upper surface prolonged inward in a broad, flat, triangular tooth.   Palm heavy, increasing in width from proximal to distal end, distal height nearly as great as superior length and twice as great as thickness; outer surface convex in a vertical direction, ornamented with a pattern of tubercles or elevations: one elongate, near and parallel to the distal end and composed of two tubercles partly or wholly fused; a round boss at the center; above it two slender, pear-shaped tubercles, pointing obliquely toward the carpus; above the lower margin on the proximal half there is a row of four slender, irregular-shaped tubercles, the proximal one crescentic, the next one an inverted V, the others linear.   Upper and lower margins thick; on the inner surface below the upper margin and just behind the middle there is a large depressed lobe, pointing distad.   Fingers of moderate size, widely separated at base by a broad U-shaped sinus in the palm.   Fixed finger horizontal or nearly so, sometimes bent a little downward; the outer surface is depressed through its middle; the prehensile edge bears two small teeth arranged crosswise at base, followed by six teeth in single file.   Dactylus strongly arched, thick; a large basal prehensile tooth directed backward, followed by two small teeth.   Ambulatory legs narrow; only the merus is preserved.

Measurements: Holotype, approximate length of carapace, 17.6 millimeters; width of same, 24.8 millimeters; fronto-orbital width, 13 millimeters; width of front, 5.3 millimeters.   Largest carapace, width, 35.4 millimeters.   Palm, middle length to sinus, 15.7 millimeters; superior length, 14 millimeters; distal height, 13.6 millimeters.   Largest palm, height, 17.2 millimeters.

Relation: This species seems to be nearest to *X. bavaricus* Lörenthey[47] from the Eocene of Bavaria.   Whereas the general shape of the carapace

---

[47] E. Lörenthey: *Beiträge zur decapodenfauna des Ungarischen Tertiars*, Természetrajzi Füzetek, vol. 21 (1898) p. 142, pl. 11, figs. 2a–2e, 3a, 3b.

and the outline of front and antero-lateral margin are similar in the two species, *X. bavaricus* lacks the small round bosses of *alabamensis* and also the ornamentation of the palm.

Occurrence: Alabama; Sucarnoochee beds, Midway:

Prairie Creek, Allenton and Pine Barren section, Wilcox County; L. C. Johnson, collector (Coll. Nos. 264, 281, 284); many specimens; Cat. Nos. 371690, 371694, 371699, 371707. One carapace with right cheliped attached is holotype (Cat. No. 371708).

Pine Barren Creek, Wilcox County; L. C. Johnson, collector; one fragment.

Estelle, Wilcox County; one specimen.

Collections: U. S. National Museum, type, Cat. No. 371708; Alabama Museum of Natural History.

Genus PANOPEUS Milne Edwards
Panopeus estellensis Rathbun, n.sp.
(Plate 16, figures 17, 18)

Two dactyls of right major chelipeds; the smaller is the holotype. The dactyl is rather high throughout its length until near the tip where it rapidly diminishes. The basal tooth is large, and directed backward; of the five remaining teeth, the first and the third are somewhat larger than the others. On the outer surface a little above the middle a longitudinal row of fine punctae with larger ones at intervals; on the inner surface a similar row similarly placed but in a shallow groove. Other scattered punctae are inconspicuous.

The paratype is the same shape as the holotype; it has lost its outer layer and shows no markings; the basal tooth is wide but reduced in length; it is followed by seven smaller teeth, of which the second and the fourth are the largest.

Length of holotype, 6 millimeters.

In shape these fingers resemble those of mature specimens of the Recent *P. occidentalis*.[48] In *occidentalis* there is on each side of the finger a row of punctae near the upper margin and another half way between that row and the prehensile teeth.

Occurrence: Alabama: Estelle, Wilcox County; Sucarnoochee beds, Midway, lower Eocene; holotype and paratype.

Collection: Alabama Museum of Natural History; types.

Genus GALENOPSIS A. Milne Edwards
Galenopsis americana Rathbun, n.sp.
(Plate 21, figures 19–22)

One palm of right chela, the distal extremity lacking, also a part of the outer surface. Greatest height (14.5 millimeters) about equal to superior

[48] M. J. Rathbun: *The cancroid crabs of America*, U. S. Nat. Mus., Bull. 152 (1930) p. 348, pl. 161.

length; height diminishes toward proximal end. Palm thick, lower surface evenly rounded from outer to inner surface; upper margin bending inward in its proximal half where it is bluntly carinate. Outer surface evenly rounded and in large part ornamented with a pattern of low reticulating ridges; inner surface uneven, highest in the middle, depressed above the lower margin, and below the distal portion of the upper margin and again below the proximal end. Surface finely granulate above, and finely punctate on the reticulating ridges.

The external pattern suggests that represented by A. Milne Edwards[49] for *G. murchisonii*, but the shape is more that of Stolíczka's figures[50] of the same species.

Occurrence: Alabama: Pine Barren region, Wilcox County; Sucarnoochee beds, Midway, lower Eocene; L. C. Johnson, collector; one right palm.

Collection: U. S. National Museum; type, Cat. No. 371743.

Family XANTHIDAE
Genus and species undetermined
(Plate 24, figure 29)

A merus of a left ambulatory leg of a large species; compressed, outer surface convex, inner surface less so, having a shallow longitudinal depression on the upper half; lower margin straight, upper arcuate; both ends broken off. Lower surface and lower half of outer surface rough with separated granules sunk in pits or sockets, the granules directed distad. Upper half of outer surface and all of the inner surface except the depression, covered with small, inconspicuous scattered sockets. Length (incomplete), 26.2 millimeters; width at middle, 9.6 millimeters.

This merus resembles in shape those of *Ocalina*, but the surface of those appears smooth.

Occurrence: Alabama: Pine Barren Creek, Wilcox County; Midway, lower Eocene; L. C. Johnson, collector (7–11); one specimen.

Collection: Alabama Museum of Natural History.

Genus PLAGIOLOPHUS Bell
Plagiolophus bakeri Rathbun, n.sp.
(Plate 21, figure 23)

Represented by one specimen showing the carapace only. Carapace divided into 14 unequal and irregular raised areas covered with disc-like granules mostly of large size but with some smaller ones near the edges;

---

[49] A. Milne Edwards: *Monographie des crustacés fossiles de la famille des cancériens*, Ann. Sci. Nat., Zool., ser. 5, vol. 3 (1865) pl. 9, fig. 1c.

[50] F. Stolíczka: *Observations on fossil crabs from Tertiary deposits in Sind and Kutch*, Geol. Surv. India, Mem., Palaeontol. Indica, ser. 7, vol. 1, no. 14, pt. 1 (1871) pl. 3, figs. 2c, 2d.

five are gastric, three of them large and subtriangular, the mesogastric elevation not prolonged on the narrow part of that subregion, epigastric lobes small; hepatic area small, oblong, parallel to the antero-lateral margin; branchial areas, three, the anterior obliquely transverse, the intermediate one small, situated at inner angle, the posterior one large, subquadrilateral, prolonged in a point toward the postero-lateral angle of the carapace. Disc-like granules also ornament the dorsal surface of the front and orbits and of the last two lateral teeth. Front subtruncate, medially furrowed; orbits oblique and with two superior closed fissures, indicated by furrows. Antero-lateral margin slightly arcuate, with four teeth not counting the orbital tooth; the first is low, formed by the continuation of a suborbital ridge and is armed with stout, blunt spinules; the other three are small but dentiform, and armed to some extent with spinules; lower surface of carapace rough with short spinules or pointed granules, and behind the second lateral tooth projecting sideways beyond the dorsal surface. A row of fine granules along the posterior margin; on either side above the margin a small cluster of little larger granules. Grooves between granulated areas deep and smooth and covered with minute punctae.

Measurements: Holotype, length of carapace, 17.3 millimeters; width at last lateral tooth, 19.7 millimeters; width at subbranchial regions, 20.3 millimeters; fronto-orbital width, 14.3 millimeters; width of front, 5.4 millimeters.

Relation: The ornamentation of the carapace is similar in character to that of the Cretaceous *P. formosus*[51] (Reuss) although the areas are of different shape and arrangement. The lateral margin is produced in *formosus* to a pronounced lateral angle, whereas that of *bakeri* is almost longitudinal behind the second tooth.

Occurrence: Texas: Moseley's Ferry, northwestern Brazos County; Cook Mountain formation of the lower Claiborne of the horizon of the Moseley Ferry beds, upper Eocene; gift of Charles L. Baker, Houston; one specimen.

Collection: U. S. National Museum; type; Cat. No. 371574.

Family MAJIDAE
Genus STENOCIONOPS (Leach ms.) Desmarest
Stenocionops suwanneeana Rathbun, n.sp.

(Plate 21, figures 1-3)

Holotype and only specimen: A left propodus of cheliped showing the greater part of the palm and a fragment of the immovable finger. Palm two and a half times as long, measured through the middle, as its greatest

---

[51] *Glyphithyreus formosus* Reuss. A. E. Reuss: *Zur kenntniss fossiler krabben,* Denksch. k. Akad. Wiss. math. natur. Cl., vol. 17 (1859) p. 4, pl. 2, figs. 1-3. *Plagiolophus formosus.* A. Milne Edwards: *Monographie des crustacés fossiles de la famille des cancériens,* Ann. Sci. Nat., Zool., ser. 5, vol. 3 (1865) p. 332, pl. 10, figs. 1, 1a.

height; it is lowest at the proximal end and increases gradually to the distal end, except for a slight swelling along the middle of the lower margin. Upper and lower margins thick and broadly rounded and showing an indication of fine irregular granulation. Palm thickest along the middle line; on both the outer and the inner surfaces there is a blunt, longitudinal elevation which slopes gradually to the upper and the lower margins; at the middle the thickness is two-thirds as great as the height; the surface inside and out is covered with low irregular elongate granules or tubercles arranged crosswise of the palm and to some extent forming clusters which range roughly in three or four longitudinal series. The surface near the fingers is depressed and almost smooth; below the finger it is plainly granulate. The immovable finger is directed slightly downward; it is relatively small, its basal thickness and height subequal; it tapers rapidly; the tip is lacking.

Measurements: Length of propodus, below, 33 millimeters; above, 24.5 millimeters; at middle, 30 millimeters. Height at distal end of palm, 11.8 millimeters; at proximal end, 9.5 millimeters; at middle, 10.7 millimeters; thickness at middle, 7.2 millimeters.

Relation: Shape of palm akin to, but much shorter than, that of Recent S. furcata (Olivier)[52] found on the coast of Georgia and Florida.

Occurrence:

Florida: Rowland's Bluff, Suwannee County; Ocala limestone, Eocene; L. C. Johnson, collector (Coll. No. 365), U. S. Geological Survey.

Collection: U. S. National Museum; type, Cat. No. 137885.

OLIGOCENE

Order DECAPODA

Family CALLIANASSIDAE
Genus CALLIANASSA Leach
Callianassa berryi Rathbun, n.sp.

(Plate 21, figures 12–14)

Holotype a right manus. Upper and lower margins subparallel, curving toward each other at the proximal end, which is vertical. Distal margin at articulation of dactylus also vertical. Lower distal end of palm lacking. Outer surface much more convex than the inner, its lower two-fifths covered with large, separated granules or round sockets. Lower edge thin, compressed, blunt, without ornamentation on the outer face; on the inner face close to the edge there is a row of about 12 oblique sockets with a few smaller ones interspersed; they are sublinear in shape, and have a tuberculiform base near the edge of the palm, followed distally by an oblong depression; the larger of these depressions doubtless held a tuft of hairs,

---

[52] M. J. Rathbun: *The spider crabs of America*, U. S. Nat. Mus., Bull. 129 (1925) p. 449, pls. 160 and 161.

the smaller ones a single hair. The inner surface has a depression in its lower distal portion. The lower two-thirds of this surface is covered with coarse granules like those on the outer surface. The distal third of the upper margin is thick and broadly rounded; but further back the margin is surmounted by a thin, narrow edge; on the inner side of this there are about six small punctae with unequal intervals; in the same line, but on the distal third, are the bases of two stout spines, one at the end of the rim, the outer half way between that point and the distal end of the segment; on the outer side of the upper margin four small punctae can be discerned. At the distal end of the inner surface, bordering the articulation, there is a narrow band of fine granules. Higher up the articulating condyle is prominent. The corresponding edge of the outer surface is broken away except at the lower end, where it is granulated.

Relation: Distinguished from other species with a square-built palm by the great roughness of both inner and outer surfaces, the presence of two strong spines on the upper margin and of a row of obliquely placed sockets along the inner surface of the lower margin.

Measurements: Length of palm from interdigital sinus measured along inner surface, 17.8 millimeters; greatest width, 16.2 millimeters; width of dactylar opening, or thickness of palm at distal end, 5.3 millimeters; greatest thickness of propodal finger, measured on the adjacent palm, 3 millimeters.

Occurrence: Mississippi at Vicksburg, Warren County; Glendon limestone, Vicksburg group, Oligocene; loaned by E. W. Berry.

Collection: Johns Hopkins University; type.

Callianassa vaughani Rathbun

See page 104.

Family RANINIDAE
Genus RANINA Lamarck
Ranina georgiana Rathbun, n.sp.
(Plate 21, figures 7, 8)

A carapace with the anterior and the posterior ends incomplete; convex from side to side, much less so from front to back; lateral margins strongly arcuate, postero-lateral margins nearly straight viewed from above. The ornamentation consists of transverse pectinated ridges, each point of which shows a minute pit; the points are separated by short longitudinal furrows. These raised lines begin at the lateral margin; some are continued across the carapace, others terminate not far from the middle, and overlap one another. Each ridge is accentuated by a narrow groove in front of it. The base of the rostrum has a median carina with a groove on either side and a raised margin; on the left side a short, broad tooth is visible on the orbital margin. At least five short spines on antero-lateral margin.

The ornamentation of the dorsal surface is similar to that of *R. porifera*

Woodward,[53] but is coarser, the transverse lines farther apart. In *R. georgiana* there are 17 lines, counting along the left side, whereas in *R. porifera* 17 lines occupy not more than two-thirds the length of the carapace.

Measurements: Length of carapace of type (incomplete), 30.6 millimeters; greatest width, 25.6 millimeters.

A larger specimen, 40 millimeters wide, from Alabama was received later. The outer angle of the front terminates in a spine (tip broken) which appears to overreach the remainder of the front. The lateral margin between second and third carinae shows a pair of spines the posterior of which is longer, stouter, and more curved.

Occurrence: Georgia; Glendon limestone, Vicksburg, lower Oligocene:

FIGURE 2.—*Ranina georgiana*

Alabama, Oligocene. United States National Museum, Catalogue Number 372809. Natural size.

Old factory about 1½ miles above Bainbridge, Decatur County; 1920; T. W. Vaughan, collector (Coll. No. 3397).

Alabama; Glendon limestone: St. Stephens Bluff, Tombigbee River, Clarke County; C. W. Cooke, W. H. Monroe, and R. B. Stewart, Coll. No. 12168; Cat. No. 372809.

Collection: U. S. National Museum, type, Cat. No. 371714.

Family PORTUNIDAE
Genus CALLINECTES Stimpson
Callinectes alabamensis Rathbun, n.sp.

(Plate 21, figures 4–6)

Holotype a left manus, incomplete and with the inner surface lacking. Upper surface level, with a blunt longitudinal carina on either side; the

---

[53] H. Woodward: *On the oldest known British crab (Palaeinachus longipes) from the Forest Marble, Malmesbury, Wilts*, Geol. Soc. London, Quart. Jour., vol. 22 (1866) p. 592, pl. 26, fig. 18.

surface becomes narrower in the proximal half, the outer carina sinuous in dorsal view and more so in side view, the distal half dipping downward; both carinae terminate distally in a stout spine. On the outer surface there are three blunt carinae which converge from the distal to the proximal end, the middle one the strongest, terminating abruptly a short distance behind the interdigital sinus; the lowest carina gradually fades out toward the carpus. A strong articulating condyle just below the end of the upper carina. Lower surface broadly rounded, increasing in width proximally from the finger end. Surface finely and closely granulate and with scattered punctae of variable size.

Measurements: Height of palm, 13.7 millimeters; length, incomplete, 21.2 millimeters; approximate thickness, 6.6 millimeters.

Relation: Near *C. reticulatus*[54] of Panama but with a different surface, granulated instead of reticulated, lateral carinae more convergent, upper surface wider in its distal half instead of narrower.

Occurrence: Alabama; Byram marl?, Vicksburg group, Oligocene: Perdue Hill, Monroe County; loaned by E. W. Berry.

Collection: Johns Hopkins University; type.   *39957*

Genus NECRONECTES A. Milne Edwards
Necronectes vaughani[55] Rathbun, n.sp.
(Plate 22, figures 7–11)

Carapace about two-thirds as long as wide, high in the middle, sloping down in all directions toward the border. Metagastric region highest, a little in front of the middle of the carapace. Behind this point on the branchial region there is an oblique row of three subparallel prominences, the anterior one the larger, close to the cervical suture, the second one rounder, the third narrow and elongate. The furrow behind the anterior swelling is prolonged outward for a short distance parallel to the cervical suture. At the inner angle of the branchial region there is a small round boss or tubercle bordered on the inner side by a curved linear elevation. The protogastric regions form each a large smooth elevation. Cardiac region only partially divided by a narrow and shallow median furrow. The groove separating the branchial from the metagastric and the anterior cardiac regions is deep. Hepatic region depressed and scarcely separable from the neighboring regions. A broad median furrow extends from the mesogastric region to frontal margin. Surface finely and densely granulate. Front wider and more advanced than orbit, armed with four spines, two of which are close together at middle and divergent, the others at the outer angles and forming the inner boundary of the orbit. Orbit rather deeply cut, outer tooth less advanced than inner; next it a shallow tooth

[54] M. J. Rathbun: *Decapod crustaceans from the Panama region*, U. S. Nat. Mus., Bull. 103 (1919) p. 163, pl. 66, figs. 5–7.

[55] Named for Dr. T. Wayland Vaughan, for many years in charge of Coastal Plain investigations of the U. S. Geological Survey.

marked on either side by a deep linear impression.   Between this tooth and the front a broader more advanced tooth separated by a wide interval. The antero-lateral teeth increase in width from the first to the eighth; they are subtriangular and trend forward except the eighth which is directed outward, is narrower than the preceding, and is surmounted by a blunt ridge prolonged inward for a little on the carapace.

Buccal cavity with parallel sides; ischium of outer maxilliped with a deep longitudinal groove nearer the inner than the outer margin; exognath as wide as outer section of endognath.   Lower surface of carapace broad, sternum correspondingly narrow, narrower than in *Portunus*, coarsely granulate, a large boss near the attachment of the cheliped; margin just anterior to the cheliped much swollen.   Merus of cheliped stout; immovable finger stout, smooth outside and beneath, not carinate, but with a shallow, punctate, longitudinal depression through the middle.

Measurements: Holotype, median length of carapace, 45.3 millimeters; length to tip of submedian spine, 47.4 millimeters; width of front, 10.2 millimeters; width of orbit, that is, from tip of outer tooth of front to tip of outer tooth of orbit, 7.6 millimeters; width of carapace at base of posterior lateral tooth, 66 millimeters; Florida carapace, length from posterior margin to anterior end of mesogastric region, 54 millimeters.

Occurrence: Lower Oligocene:

Mississippi: Vicksburg, Warren County; Glendon limestone, Vicksburg; two carapaces (one is holotype); loaned by E. W. Berry.   From hard ledge at Glass Bayou; October 18, 1912; C. W. Cooke, collector (6446); three specimens, incomplete, Cat. No. 371728.

Mississippi: Southeast corner of northwest quarter of northeast quarter, Section 22, Township 5 North, Range 3 East; within town limits of Brandon; on State highway 18; Pelahatchee quadrangle; Glendon limestone, Vicksburg; M. A. Pentz, collector; one specimen showing ventral surface; loaned by Johns Hopkins University.

Florida: Marianna, Jackson County; Marianna limestone in quarry; D. S. Mossom, collector; one specimen of carapace considerably larger than any other but lacking all the dentate margins; Cat. No. 371697.

Collections: U. S. National Museum; Johns Hopkins University, type.

MIOCENE

Order DECAPODA

Family CALLIANASSIDAE
Genus CALLIANASSA Leach
Callianassa floridana Rathbun, n.sp.

(Plate 24, figures 1–11)

The material consists of upwards of 40 fingers, movable and immovable, representing chiefly the major chela.   The major dactylus is about three times as long as wide, the prehensile edge finely and closely denticulate and interrupted at middle by a broad, subrectangular cut and by a narrower notch at the articulating end; between the two is formed a broad truncate tooth. On the outer surface on the lower half there is a longitudinal row of four large equidistant sockets at the level of the top of the middle notch, two sockets on either side of the notch. A little below the upper margin and above the penult socket of the lower row there is a single large socket. Upper margin bluntly carinate in proximal half; immediately below it a row of eight or more sockets ending at finger tip. Below the distal third of these sockets a narrow carina bearing a row of eight or ten minute sockets. A broad smooth ridge extends through the middle of the inner surface; a single socket at its middle. A row of three sockets above lower margin, two on the distal half, the third on the proximal half.

The major propodal or immovable finger is narrow, the prehensile edge swollen at the middle in a low broad tooth. Outer surface with a row of three sockets unevenly spaced above the lower margin; just outside the prehensile margin a row of seven sockets, the distal one not far from the tip. Prehensile edge smoothly carinate, except at the proximal end where there is a row of granules; the carina is set off by a groove on the inner surface, which is bordered by a longitudinal raised area which may, or may not, have a linear shallow depression through its distal half or two-thirds and which at its proximal end is coarsely granulate, the granulation extending variably, but usually about a third the length of the finger; on the inner side of the lower margin there is a row of approximately 12 sockets, placed closer together on the proximal half.

A few small fingers associated with those described above are thought to be dactyls of minor chelipeds. The outer surface has three large punctae in a row parallel to the lower margin, also a fourth puncta above the interval between the two proximal punctae and a little below the upper margin. Upper margin thick, bearing along its inner side about nine punctae, those at the proximal end smaller and closer than the others; alongside and lower down on the inner surface there is a short, acute carina rough with fine granules; on the lower half of the surface there is a row of three punctae, the proximal interspace the longer; above this interspace and midway to the upper margin there is a single socket.

Measurements: Length of large major dactyl, holotype, 12.5 millimeters; of large major propodal finger, 9.6 millimeters; of largest minor dactyl, 7 millimeters.

Relation: The shape of the prehensile margin of the major dactyl of the chela is similar to that of *C. latidigita*[56] from the lower Miocene of Santo Domingo, but the latter is thicker and more cylindrical; the immovable finger is much shorter and more triangular than in the Floridian species.

[56] M. J. Rathbun: *West Indian Tertiary decapod crustaceans*, Carnegie Inst. Washington, Pub. 291 (1919) p. 165, pl. 9, figs. 10 and 11.

Occurrence: Florida: Chipola formation, Alum Bluff group, lower Miocene:

Calhoun County: one mile below Bailey's Ferry on Chipola River; from banks of river above white limestone bed; Frank Burns, collector (Coll. No. 2213); one dactyl of minor chela (Cat. No. 371467).

Liberty County: Lower bed at Alum Bluff on Apalachicola River; calcareous red sand bed; 1889; Frank Burns, collector (Coll. No. 2211); type lot.

Collection: U. S. National Museum; type, Cat. No. 371469.

Callianassa matsoni Rathbun, n.sp.

(Plate 24, figures 23-28)

Four examples of a nearly smooth, subrectangular, convex palm with a narrow immovable finger. Holotype, outer surface exposed: palm slightly longer than greatest height, which diminishes little from the proximal to the distal end. Outer surface convex in a vertical direction. Base of finger not more than one-third height of palm; above it a deep U-shaped sinus; the distal lobe of the palm below the articulation with the dactylus is oblique-perpendicular, bordered by a row of large granules and with a short stout tooth near the lower end of its distal surface. Above the lower margin of the palm, a row of about 12 small sockets; a larger socket in same line on finger; a socket above and one below the digital sinus; a row of sockets below the prehensile edge of the propodal finger.

Paratypes: These show granulation on the outer surface of the palm for a short distance about the sinus; also a few granules on the inner surface of the lobe as well as along its margin. The upper surface of the palm is thick and smoothly rounded except at the proximal end, where it forms on the inner side a thin edge which is bent inward; only two punctae are visible on this surface. Two of the three paratypes have the stump of the finger in line with the lower margin of the palm instead of inclined downward a little as in the holotype; the lower margin of the palm is straight and at right angles to the proximal margin, the upper margin is slightly arched, the distal height a little less than the proximal; furthermore, the upper margin is carinated for at least half its length. From 15 to 17 sockets along the inner side of the lower margin. On the inner surface below the distal end of the upper margin, a row of three sockets slanting downward toward the dactyl. These two specimens appear to belong to the chelipeds of the female or to the minor chelipeds of the male.

Associated with these are two detached movable fingers, one of which is complete. It is stout and armed with three teeth or lobes on the prehensile edge, two close together near the proximal end and one smaller near the tip. The sockets are obscure but number four or five on the upper surface, one just below and outside near proximal end, four on the outer surface above the lower edge, and three in a similar position on the inner surface.

A third finger from Columbia County is similar to the preceding and is accompanied by a wrist of a small cheliped which may belong to this species. It is broader than long, upper and lower edges thin and sharp, outer surface with a few minute sockets along lower margin, one near the middle of upper margin, three widely separated along proximal margin. On the inner surface two sockets are visible along upper margin.

Measurements: Holotype, right major palm, length to middle of distal lobe, 18.5 millimeters; proximal height, 14.3 millimeters; distal height, 13.7 millimeters; height of finger at base, 4.6 millimeters.

Occurrence:

Florida; U. S. Geological Survey:

Wakulla County: Sopchoppy; Chipola formation;[57] September 8, 1913; George C. Matson, collector (Coll. No. 7468); one right major palm, holotype (Cat. No. 371470).

Hamilton County: White Springs; Chipola formation. At water level at wagon bridge (Suwannee River); 1908; George C. Matson, collector (4976); one right (minor?) palm (Cat. No. 371471).

Columbia County: Spring on left bank of Suwannee River about 100 yards above Rock Island and about half a mile above White Springs; No. 3 of section; Chipola formation: November 4, 1913; T. W. Vaughan, E. H. Sellards, and C. W. Cooke, collectors (C-92-13) 6776; one right movable finger and left wrist; Cat. No. 371464.

Marion County; midway between Anthony and Martin, just east of cross roads; Tampa limestone; C. W. Cooke, collector (7353); right and left palm; Cat. No. 371893.

Florida: exact locality not given; one left major palm, one right (minor?) palm, two movable fingers; Cat. No. 371463.

Collection: U. S. National Museum; type, Cat. No. 371470.

Callianassa suffolkensis Rathbun, n.sp.

(Plate 24, figures 20–22)

Two right movable fingers, distinguished by unusually prominent carinae, of which there are two on the inner surface, two above, one outside, in addition to the acute prehensile edge.   Inner carinae blunt and smooth, the lower one narrow and near the prehensile granules, the upper one twice as broad and a little above the middle; in the intervening furrow, nine small sockets; in the upper furrow of the inner surface, four large evenly spaced sockets on the proximal two-thirds. On the upper surface the innermost carina is narrow and high; on the inner side of its proximal third there is a row of small irregular punctae; the outer carina of the upper

[57] C. Wythe Cooke [*Geology of Florida*, Florida Geol. Surv., 20th Ann. Rept., 1927-28 (1929) p. 116] refers Sopchoppy and White Springs to the Hawthorn formation.

surface is acute and sinuous and rough with about 15 unequal sockets on its inner slope; its outer slope is deeper, leading to the carina of the outer surface and is rough with sockets, two or three deep.   Outer carina running through the middle, and smooth, broad, and high; below it there are roughly two rows of punctae.   Prehensile edge shows about 19 crowded granules in the inner surface, but viewed from outside appears sharp and crenulate except at the proximal fourth.

Measurements: Length of type finger above, 7 millimeters; greatest width of outer surface, 2.3 millimeters.   A paratype incomplete measures 3.2 millimeters in its greatest width.

Occurrence: Virginia; Yorktown formation, upper part: Nansemond County: U. S. Geological Survey:

Three miles northeast of Suffolk; one right movable finger, holotype (Cat. No. 166064).

Two and a half miles northwest of Suffolk; proximal two-thirds of right movable finger, paratype (Cat. No. 166063).

Collection: U. S. National Museum; type, Cat. No. 166064.

Callianassa atlantica Rathbun

1873. *Callianassa stimpsoni*.   Smith, U. S. Commr. of Fish and Fisheries, Rept. for 1871–1872, pt. 1, p. 549 [255], pl. 2, fig. 8; not *C. stimpsonii* Gabb, Palaeontology of California, vol. 1, sec. 4 (1864) p. 57, pl. 9, fig. 1, *a, b, c.*
1926. *Callianassa atlantica*.   Rathbun, U. S. Nat. Mus., Bull. 138, p. 107; Recent.

Occurrence:
Virginia: Isle of Wight County: Three quarters of a mile north of Zuni; Yorktown formation; one immovable finger of major chela (Cat. No. 166065).
Virginia: Nansemond County: half a mile below Suffolk waterworks dam; Yorktown formation, upper part; one movable finger of major chela (Cat. No. 166067).
North Carolina: Bertie County: Colerain Landing, Chowan River; Yorktown formation; three immovable fingers of major chelae (Cat. No. 166066).
Collection: U. S. National Museum.
Type localities: Long Island Sound to Southern States; Recent.

Callianassa vaughani Rathbun

(Plate 26, figures 6, 7)

1918. *Callianassa vaughani*.   Rathbun, U. S. Nat. Mus., Bull. 103, p. 148, pl. 63, figs. 10–13; Panama.

Occurrence: Mexico; River Bank, San Fernando, in east-central Tamaulipas.   March 3, 1907.   Upper Oligocene-Miocene.   One palm, two movable fingers.
Collection: University of Texas.

Family PAGURIDAE
Genus PETROCHIRUS Stimpson
Petrochirus inequalis Rathbun

(Plate 23, figure 6)

1919. *Petrochirus inequalis*.   Rathbun, Carnegie Inst. Washington, Publ. 291, p. 167, pl. 9, figs. 13–15; type-locality, Amina River, Yaqui Valley, Santo Domingo; lower Miocene.[58]

[58] Oligocene (Glaessner).   M. F. Gl e sner: *Fossilium catalogus*, 1.   Animalia, pars 41 (1929) p. 312.

Occurrence: Florida: Calhoun County: north bank of Tenmile Creek at wagon bridge on road from Forestville to Marianna, probably about 20 miles from Marianna; Chipola formation, lower Miocene; November 18, 1914; C. W. Cooke and W. C. Mansfield, collectors (7151); U. S. Geological Survey; a much worn left propodal finger (distal half); Cat. No. 371466.

Collection: U. S. National Museum; type, Cat. No. 324467.

Petrochirus bouvieri Rathbun

1911. "*Petrochirus cf. granulatus Olivier sp.*" Toula, Jahrb. der k. k. Geolog. Reichsanstalt, Wien, vol. 61, p. 511 [25], pl. 30 [1], fig. 13; Gatun; Middle Miocene.

1918. *Petrochirus bouvieri.* Rathbun, U. S. Nat. Mus., Bull. 103, p. 153.

The clusters of tubercles on the fingers are crowded close together, mostly of large size, no small clusters or single tubercles interspersed; the clusters in general are broader than long in the direction of their axes, they consist of 12 to 15 tubercles in addition to a row of granules on the distal border.

Occurrence: Florida: Liberty County; probably upper Miocene (in Florida); U. S. Geological Survey: On Evans farm, Section 6, Township 2 South, Range 6 West, half a mile east of Evans and about 4 miles south of Hosford; obtained at about water level of Telogia Creek; November 6, 1925; W. C. Mansfield, collector (1/957); fingers of left cheliped of a large specimen; Cat. No. 371260.

Collection: U. S. National Museum.

Type: Geological collection, Vienna Technical University.

Genus PAGURISTES Dana
Paguristes chipolensis Rathbun, n.sp.

(Plate 24, figures 12-15)

The dactylus of a right chela and the propodus of a right ambulatory leg: Upper surface of dactylus about $2\frac{1}{2}$ times as long as its greatest width; prehensile edge with a large tubercle at proximal end, followed by a row of about 16 small granules which diminish successively in size and disappear before reaching tip of finger; outer margin marked by a row of 11 rather large separated granules; near the prehensile edge an irregular row of eight or nine granules alternating with punctae; between the outer and inner rows are smaller scattered granules which form roughly two rows. Outer surface rough with raised sockets, the upper row of about 13 alternating large and small, the next row of seven or eight; this is followed by a row of nine simple punctae. Lower surface with two rows of punctae.

Propodus of ambulatory leg armed with short stout spines above and below; inner surface covered with acute tubercles and granules; outer surface rough with reticulating elevations, and having a depressed punctate line through the center and a row of punctae above the lower margin.

Measurements: Length of dactylus of right chela, holotype, 5.2 millimeters; greatest width, 2 millimeters. Length of propodus of ambulatory 5.4 millimeters; width, 1.7 millimeters.

Occurrence: Florida: Calhoun County: one mile below Bailey's Ferry on Chipola River; from banks of river above white limestone bed; Chipola formation, Alum Bluff group, lower Miocene; Frank Burns, collector (2213).

Collection: U. S. National Museum; type, Cat. No. 371465.

Family CALAPPIDAE
Genus CALAPPA Weber
Calappa flammea (Herbst)

1794. *Cancer flammeus.* Herbst, Natur. Krabben u. Krebse, vol. 2, p. 161, pl. 40, fig. 2.
1901. *Calappa flammea.* Rathbun, U. S. Fish Comm. for 1900, Bull., vol. 20, pt. 2, p. 84, pl. 2, and synonymy; Recent.

Occurrence: Florida:
Okaloosa County: West bank of Yellow River, half a mile east of postoffice, Oak Grove; Oak Grove sand, Alum Bluff group, middle Miocene; Frank Burns, collector (2646); a dactylus of the right, major chela of a small specimen; Cat. No. 135917.
Okaloosa County: Oak Grove bridge, base of bluff, Yellow River; Oak Grove sand; 1908; T. W. Vaughan, collector (5631); one major finger; Cat. No. 371455.
Okaloosa County: Right bank of Yellow River, 400 feet below the bridge near Oak Grove; Oak Grove sand; October 20, 1914; T. W. Vaughan, C. W. Cooke, and W. C. Mansfield, collectors (7054); two major fingers; Cat. No. 371452.
Walton County: Shell marl, Vaughans Creek [locally, Blounts Creek], 6 miles south of DeFuniak Springs; Choctawhatchee marl, upper part of middle Miocene; Florida Geological Survey; fingers of a right chela; returned to sender.
Walton County: Shell Bluff, Section 4, Township 3 North, Range 21 West; high bluff back from Shoal River; Shoal River formation, Alum Bluff group, middle Miocene; Frank Burns, collector (3742); one major finger; Cat. No. 371454.
Washington County: Near water level at Boynton Landing, on Choctawhatchee River, 35½ miles by water from mouth of river, probably about 18 miles by land from Caryville, 32 miles by water; Chipola formation, Alum Bluff group, lower Miocene; E. H. Sellards, collector (7893); two fragments of fingers; Cat. No. 371453.
Calhoun County: One mile below Bailey's Ferry, on the Chipola River; from river banks above white limestone bed; Chipola formation; Frank Burns, collector (2213); three major fingers; Cat. No. 371451.
Collections: U. S. National Museum, Florida Geological Survey.
Type: Not extant; Recent.

Family LEUCOSIIDAE
Genus PERSEPHONA Leach
Persephona punctata (Linnaeus)

1758. *Cancer punctatus.* Linnaeus, Syst. Nat., ed. 10, p. 630 (part).
1918. *Persephona punctata.* Hay and Shore, Bur. Fisheries, Bull., vol. 35, 1915–1916, p. 423, pl. 32, fig. 9, and synonymy.

Occurrence:
Virginia:
Nansemond County: At Calhoun Bridge about 3 miles northwest of Suffolk; Yorktown formation; May 22, 1922; W. C. Mansfield, collector (1/197); one arm; Cat. No. 371472.
Tidewater Railroad, 1½ miles north of Suffolk; Yorktown formation; one arm; Cat. No. 166055.
Tidewater Railroad, 1½ miles north of Suffolk; Yorktown formation; four arms; Cat. No. 166056.
One mile northeast of Suffolk; Yorktown formation; one arm; Cat. No. 166057.
Suffolk; Yorktown formation; B. L. Miller, collector; dactylus of right cheliped; Cat. No. 166061.
North Carolina:
Pitt County: 8 to 9 miles south of Greenville; Yorktown formation (?); one arm; Cat. No. 166058.
Duplin County; Magnolia; Duplin formation; one arm; Cat. No. 166060.
South Carolina:
Charleston County: Bolton Phosphate Company; Stono River; upper Miocene, formation (?); one arm; Cat. No. 166059.
Collection: U. S. National Museum.
Type: Recent.

Family PORTUNIDAE
Genus PORTUNUS Fabricius
Portunus (Portunus) sayi (Gibbes)

1850. *Lupa sayi.* Gibbes, Amer. Assoc. Adv. Sci., Pr., 3rd meeting, p. 178 [14].
1903. *Portunus (Portunus) sayi.* Rathbun, U. S. Nat. Mus., Bull. 152, p. 37, textfigs. 6 and 7, pl. 14, and synonym.

Occurrence: Florida; lower Miocene: Calhoun County; North bank of Tenmile Creek at wagon bridge on road from Forestville to Marianna, Jackson County, probably about 20 miles from Marianna; Chipola formation, Alum Bluff group; November 18, 1914; C. W. Cooke and W. C. Mansfield, collectors (7151); one right immovable finger; Cat. No. 371462.

Collection: U. S. National Museum.

Type: Not located; Recent.

Portunus, sp.

(Plate 24, figure 30)

Fingers of left claw, nearly meeting; outer layer not preserved; propodal finger over twice as long as proximal height, lower margin straight, as is also the adjacent part of the manus, grasping edge slightly sinuous, a blunt ridge above lower margin, and one less marked along the prehensile margin; dactyl not more than two-thirds as wide as fixed finger, carinated above, a blunt ridge along middle of outer surface, finger tapering gradually to tip, proximal third lacking.

Measurements: Length of prehensile edges, 24.8 millimeters; height of fixed finger at base, 10.8 millimeters.

Related, as to scarcity of ridges, to the Recent and much smaller *P. (Achelous) depressifrons* (Stimpson)[59] which is abundant on the Florida coast.

Occurrence: Florida: Gadsden County; Aspalaga Bluff, Apalachicola River, about 10 feet above river level; Tampa limestone, lower Miocene; W. C. Mansfield and G. M. Ponton, collectors (12286); Cat. No. 371892.

Collection: U. S. National Museum.

Genus CALLINECTES Stimpson
Callinectes sapidus Rathbun

1896. *Callinectes sapidus.* Rathbun, U. S. Nat. Mus., Pr., vol. 18, p. 352, pls. 12; 24, fig. 1; 25, fig. 1; 26, fig. 1; 27, fig. 1, and synonymy; Recent and fossil.

Occurrence:

Virginia: Accomac County: Gaugatha Beach; September, 1894; James P. Lucas, collector; specimen returned to sender.

U. S. Geological Survey:

Virginia: Nansemond County: One mile northeast of Suffolk, in drainage ditch; Yorktown formation; tip of left movable finger of small specimen; Cat. No. 166070.

Florida: Calhoun County: One mile below Bailey's Ferry, on Chipola River; from banks of river above white limestone bed; Chipola formation, Alum Bluff group, lower Miocene; Frank Burns, collector (2213); tip of finger; Cat. No. 371456.

Florida: Liberty County: Lower bed at Alum Bluff, on Apalachicola River; calcareous red sand bed; Chipola formation; Frank Burns, collector (2211); 15 fragments of fingers; Cat. No. 371457.

Collections: U. S. National Museum, James P. Lucas.

Type: Recent.

Genus NECRONECTES A. Milne Edwards
Necronectes drydeni Rathbun, n.sp.

(Plate 22, figures 12, 13)

A single specimen showing the carapace and the ventral surface of the body and the right arm. Carapace nearly half again as broad as long,

[59] M. J. Rathbun: *The cancroid crabs of America*, U. S. Nat. Mus., Bull. 152 (1930) p. 84, pl. 41.

slightly convex in the middle portion, lateral rim depressed especially at the hepatic region. Surface smooth, punctate. Carapace badly crushed in the gastric and frontal regions; edge of front destroyed. A furrow leads backward from either side of the mid-orbital tooth. Lateral teeth low, broader than long, except perhaps the seventh and the eighth; the latter is narrower at base than the seventh; the first tooth is small and triangular, the second to the sixth inclusive are more or less lobiform, and blunt pointed. The comparative width of the teeth is as follows: No 1 narrowest, 2 and 8, 3 and 4, 5 and 6, 7 widest. Ischium of outer maxillipeds with raised inner portion which is one-third of the width of the article and is set off by a deep groove. The abdomen is somewhat wider than in the male of *N. proavitus*[60] but probably is that of a male, as segments 4 and 5 at least are fused. The telson is longer in proportion to its width than in *proavitus*. There is a deep median groove in the sternum in front of the abdomen; there is no impressed line on the sternum between the maxillipeds, as in *proavitus* and *vaughani*. The right arm is stout, posteriorly curved, and extends laterally a little beyond the carapace.

Measurements: Length of carapace of male holotype, 57 millimeters (approximate); width of same, 84.3 millimeters; posterior length of arm, 27.6 millimeters; thickness at middle, 13.6 millimeters.

Occurrence: Maryland: Calvert County: A float about 100 feet south of Calvert Beach, probably from "zone 17"; Choptank formation; August 28, 1929, A. L. Dryden, Jr., collector.

Collection: Johns Hopkins University; type.

Genus SCYLLA DeHaan

Scylla floridana Rathbun, n.sp.

(Plate 23, figures 7, 8)

The distal half of a large right chela embracing the fingers and the articulating condyle of the palm. Distal section of palm nearly twice as high as thick; condyle bituberculate, tubercles projecting well outward, the upper proximal one smaller than the other. Fingers shaped much as in the major chela of the Recent *Scylla serrata*;[61] propodal finger considerably wider than dactyl; both are widest at base and taper gradually to a point; thick and smoothly rounded along the arcuate outer margin; prehensile margins irregularly dentate, a large tooth at base of dactyl (tip broken off), margin of fixed finger straight except at tip where it curves upward, margin of dactylus a little concave; gap between closed digits narrow, at the widest half as high as base of dactylus. There is an indication of a faint impressed longitudinal line on the propodal finger, similar to that in *serrata*. Midway

---

[60] *Gatunia proavita* Rathbun. M. J. Rathbun: *Decapod crustaceans from the Panama region*, U. S. Nat. Mus., Bull. 103 (1919) p. 168, pls. 54–56, 58, figs. 16 and 17.

[61] *Cancer serratus* Forskål. Peter Forskål: *Descriptiones animalium quae in itinere orientali observavit* (1775) p. 90.

of the height of the palm at the break there is a small elevation which may be the beginning of a ridge.

Measurements: Estimated height of palm at distal end, 32.6 millimeters; thickness, 18.2 millimeters; length of fingers on prehensile margins, 42.6 millimeters; basal height of propodal finger, 17.4 millimeters; basal height of dactylus, 14 millimeters.

Occurrence: Florida: East bank of Apalachicola River along Florida Highway 1, Chattahoochee, Gadsden County; near top of Tampa limestone here exposed; April 13, 1931, G. M. Ponton and W. C. Mansfield, collectors.

Collection: U. S. National Museum; type, Cat. No. 371717.

Family CANCRIDAE
Genus CANCER Linnaeus
Cancer borealis Stimpson

1930. *Cancer borealis*.   Rathbun, U. S. Nat. Mus., Bull. 152, p. 182, fig. 30, and synonymy.

Occurrence: Virginia: Just below Old Grove wharf, left bank of James River, about 2 miles below Camp Wallace, James City County; lowest bed; lower part of Yorktown formation.   W. C. Mansfield, collector (1/470a); one right propodal finger; Cat. No. 371461.
Collection: U. S. National Museum.
Type: Not extant; Recent.

Cancer irroratus Say

1817. *Cancer irroratus*.   Say, Philadelphia Acad. Nat. Sci., Jour., vol. 1, p. 39, pl. 4, fig. 2 (part, male).

Occurrence: Maryland: Plum Point, Calvert County, Chesapeake Bay; Calvert formation; Martin Burkenroad, collector; one movable finger of large specimen; Cat. No. 372808.
Collection: U. S. National Museum.
Type: Not extant; Recent.

Cancer proavitus Packard

1900. *Cancer proavitus*.   Packard, Amer. Acad. Arts and Sci., Pr., vol. 36, p. 3, pl. 1, fig. 1–3.
1900. *Cancer proavitus*.   Packard, Amer. Assoc. Adv. Sci., Pr., vol. 49, p. 239.
1905. *Cancer proavitus*.   Cushman, Amer. Nat., vol. 39, p. 386, pl. 2, fig. 14.

Occurrence: Massachusetts: Gay Head, Marthas Vineyard; greensand layer, upper Miocene; J. B. Woodworth, U. S. Geological Survey, collector; one right palm of large size, cotype; Cat. No. 371433.
Same locality; J. H. Clarke, collector; one male cotype showing the body (Boston Society Natural History).
Collections: U. S. National Museum, cotype, Cat. No. 371433; Boston Society of Natural History, cotype.

Family XANTHIDAE
Genus MENIPPE DeHaan
Menippe floridana Rathbun, n.sp.
(Plate 22, figures 1–6)

Holotype, a large dactylus or movable finger of a left cheliped, short in proportion to its height; height at insertion, 23 millimeters; length (chord of upper margin), 43.3 millimeters; thickness at base, 11.5 millimeters. Finger curving gradually inward and thickness gradually diminishing to the tip which is large and blunt; inner, upper, and outer surfaces smooth to the touch, set with flattened close granules, inner surface considerably flattened, two irregular rows of punctae, but no grooves, on the inner and the outer surfaces.   The prehensile teeth are worn off, but there are indications of four teeth.

Occurrence: Florida; Choctawhatchee marl:

Calhoun County: Abes Spring, Chipola River; W. C. Mansfeld, collector (1/959); one right movable finger; Florida Geological Survey.

Liberty County: Hosford [formerly Coes Mill]; T. W. Vaughan, collector (3671); prehensile edge of a right immovable finger; Cat. No. 371719.

Leon County: Herveys Creek; Florida Geological Survey (8656); one left movable finger, holotype, Cat. No. 371718.

Collections: U. S. National Museum, type, Cat. No. 371718; Florida Geological Survey.

Menippe nodifrons Stimpson

1859. *Menippe nodifrons.* Stimpson, Lyc. Nat. Hist. N. Y., Ann., vol. 7, p. 53 [7].
1930. *Menippe nodifrons.* Rathbun, U. S. Nat. Mus., Bull. 152, p. 479, pl. 198, fig. 3,
      pl. 199, and synonymy; Recent.

Occurrence: Florida:
    Walton County: Shell marl, Vaughan's Creek [locally Blount's Creek], 6 miles south of De Funiak Springs; Choctawhatchee marl, upper part of middle Miocene; Florida Geological Survey; one fragment from proximal inner end of palm at articulation with wrist; returned to sender.   This insignificant piece has the characteristic thick shell of *Menippe*, and the granulation resembles that of *nodifrons* rather than of *mercenaria*.
    Liberty County: Lower bed at Alum Bluff, Apalachicola River, calcareous red sand bed; Chipola formation, Alum Bluff group, lower Miocene; 1889; Frank Burns, collector (2211), U. S. Geological Survey; two right propodal fingers; Cat. No. 371460.
    Collections: U. S. National Museum; Florida Geological Survey.
    Type: Not extant; Recent.

Genus LOBONOTUS A. Milne Edwards
Lobonotus foerstei Rathbun, n.sp.

(Plate 23, figures 9, 10)

The type specimen shows the carapace, part of the sternum, and the short basal articles of a cheliped.   The carapace lacks a margin; the regions in their shape and ornamentation indicate a *Lobonotus*.   The middle gastric region (meso- and metagastric) is circumscribed except posteriorly near median line; immediately in front of its widest point there is a small round low elevation; protogastric regions elevated; branchial region highest in a ridge nearly transverse but inclined obliquely backward toward the lateral margin; a broad depression separates the gastric and the branchial regions from the hepatic elevation; no epigastric lobes visible; a transverse break across the carapace obscures the posterior regions, but the posterior part of the branchial region is elevated.   Surface covered with small punctae and larger granules which point forward and are more numerous on the elevations than in the depressions and thin out toward the anterior border of the carapace.   Width of carapace a little more than 40 millimeters.

Occurrence: Massachusetts: Marthas Vineyard; greensand layer, upper Miocene: Gay Head cliffs: August–September 1889, A. F. Foerste and J. B. Woodworth, collectors (4008), one specimen, holotype, Cat. No. 371431; June, 1894, W. H. Dall, collectors (2606), one fragmentary specimen; Cat. No. 371432.

Collection: U. S. National Museum; type, Cat. No. 371431.

Genus PANOPEUS Milne Edwards
Panopeus herbstii Milne Edwards

1834. *Panopeus herbstii.*   Milne Edwards, Hist. Nat. Crust., vol. 1, p. 403.
1930. *Panopeus herbstii.*   Rathbun, U. S. Nat. Mus., Bull. 152, p. 335, text-figs. 52, 53, pls. 156, 157, and synonymy.

Occurrence: The specimens examined are all fingers, chiefly of rather small crabs from the Miocene. U.S. Geological Survey.

Virginia:

Westmoreland County: Nomini Cliffs; probably Calvert formation; one finger; Cat. No. 166087.

Surry County: Claremont in marl pit; fossils taken from wall of pit and picked up from weathered-out material scattered about the floor of the pit; the uppermost Miocene bed around Claremont; Yorktown formation; June 22, 1922; W. C. Mansfield, collector (1/250); one finger; Cat. No. 371475.

Southampton County: Sycamore; Yorktown formation; one finger; Cat. No. 166079.

Southampton County: Maddelys Bluff; probably Yorktown formation; one finger; Cat. No. 166080.

Nansemond County: 1½ miles southeast of Reid's Ferry; Yorktown formation; two fingers; Cat. No. 166075.

Nansemond County: 1¼ miles north of Suffolk; Yorktown formation; one finger; Cat. No. 166085.

Nansemond County: Suffolk; Yorktown formation; one finger, Cat. No. 166084.

Nansemond County: Half a mile below Suffolk Water Works Dam; Yorktown formation; one finger; Cat. No. 166075.

North Carolina:

Hertford County: Tar Ferry, Willocan Creek; Yorktown formation; L. W. Stephenson, collector; eight specimens, Cat. No. 166078; one specimen, Cat. No. 166086.

Hertford County: Mt. Pleasant Landing, Chowan River; Yorktown formation; one specimen, Cat. No. 166088.

Bertie County: Colerain Landing, Chowan River; Yorktown formation; six specimens; Cat. No. 166081.

Bertie County: Mt. Gould Landing, Chowan River; Yorktown formation; four specimens; Cat. No. 166083.

Bertie County: Half to three-quarters of a mile above Edenhouse Point, Chowan River; Yorktown formation; eight specimens; Cat. No. 166082.

Edgecombe County: Half a mile above Bell's Bridge, Tar River; probably Yorktown formation; one specimen; Cat. No. 166067.

Craven County: Neuse River, right bank about 3 miles above Cherry Point; Yorktown formation; W. C. Mansfield, collector (1/893); one specimen; Cat. No. 371474.

Robeson County: 1½ miles northeast of Fairmont; Duplin formation; one specimen; Cat. No. 166072.

Collection: U. S. National Museum.

Type: Paris Museum; Recent.

Genus EURYTIUM Stimpson
Eurytium limosum (Say)

1818. *Cancer limosa.*   Say, Philadelphia Acad. Nat. Sci., Jour., vol. 1, p. 446.
1930. *Eurytium limosum.*   Rathbun, U. S. Nat. Mus., Bull. 152, p. 423, pl. 176, figs. 1, 2, and synonymy.

Occurrence: Miocene; U. S. Geological Survey:

North Carolina: Columbus County: Lake Waccamaw; Duplin formation; three fingers; Cat. No. 166071.

Florida: Calhoun County: One mile below Bailey's Ferry, on Chipola River; from banks of river above white limestone bed; Chipola formation, Alum Bluff group, lower Miocene; Frank Burns, collector (2213); seven fingers of small specimens; Cat. No. 371458.

Florida: Liberty County: Lower bed at Alum Bluff, Apalachicola River; calcareous red sand bed; Chipola formation; 1889; Frank Burns, collector (2211); 30 fingers; Cat. No. 371459.

Collection: U. S. National Museum.

Type: Not extant; Recent.

Family GONEPLACIDAE
Genus ARCHAEOPLAX Stimpson
Archaeoplax signifera Stimpson

(Plate 23, figures 1–5)

1863. *Archaeoplax signifera.*   Stimpson, Boston Jour. Nat. Hist., vol. 7, p. 584 [2], pl. 12.

1900. *Archaeoplax signifera.*   Packard, Amer. Acad. Arts and Sci., Pr., vol. 36, p. 7, pl. 1, fig. 4, pl. 2.

1905. *Archaeoplax signifera.*   Cushman, Amer. Nat., vol. 39, p. 383, pl. 1, pl. 2, figs. 1–13.

Occurrence: Massachusetts: Marthas Vineyard, Dukes County; greensand layer, upper Miocene:

Gay Head cliffs: August–September, 1889, A. F. Foerste and J. B. Woodworth, collectors (4006, 4007, 4012, 4014), two carapaces incomplete and more than 50 fragments, Cat. Nos. 371424–371427, 371434; June, 1894, W. H. Dall, collector (2606), 15+ fragments, Cat. No. 371428.

Weyquosque Cliffs (eastern marl bed); September 1889; Foerste and Woodworth, collectors (4008); four specimens and fragments; Cat. No. 371430.

Nashaquitsa Cliffs, Chilmark Cliff Section; September 1889; J. B. Woodworth, collector (4013); two specimens; Cat. No. 371429.

Collections: U. S. National Museum; Boston Society of Natural History, types.

Family MAJIDAE
Genus EUPROGNATHA Stimpson
Euprognatha, sp.

(Plate 24, figures 16–19)

Two left dactyls of chelae.   Two longitudinal rows of punctae on outer and inner surfaces, one row on upper surface.   Prehensile teeth shallow, irregular.

Occurrence: Florida: Hosford [formerly Coes Mill], Liberty County; upper Miocene; T. W. Vaughan, collector (3671); Cat. No. 371715.

Collection: U. S. National Museum.

Genus LIBINIA Leach
Libinia emarginata Leach

1815. *Libinia emarginata.*   Leach, Zool. Misc., vol. 2, p. 130, pl. 108.

1925. *Libinia emarginata.*   Rathbun, U. S. Nat. Mus., Bull. 129, p. 311, text-figs. 103 and 104, pls. 110–113, and synonymy.

Occurrence: North Carolina: 1½ miles above Murfreesboro, Hertford County; U. S. Geological Survey; one right movable finger; Cat. No. 166069.

Collection: U. S. National Museum.

Type: British Museum; Recent.

Libinia dubia Milne Edwards

1834. *Libinia dubia.* Milne Edwards, Hist. Nat. Crust., vol. 1, p. 300, pl. 14 *bis*,
fig. 2.
1925. *Libinia dubia.* Rathbun, U. S. Nat. Mus., Bull. 129, p. 313, text-figs. 105 and
106, pls. 114, 115, 122, fig. 1, and synonymy.

Occurrence: Virginia: Nansemond County: Suffolk; Yorktown formation; B. L. Miller, U. S. Geological
Survey, collector; one right movable finger; Cat. No. 166068.
Collection: U. S. National Museum.
Type: Paris Museum: Recent.

Order STOMATOPODA

Family CHLORIDELLIDAE
Genus GONODACTYLUS Latreille
Gonodactylus oerstedii Hansen

1895. *Gonodactylus oerstedii.* Hansen, Isopoden, Cumaceen u. Stomatopoden der
Plankton-Exped., p. 65; Recent.
The bispinose tip of the process from the peduncle of the right uropod or appen-
dage of sixth abdominal segment of a large specimen.

Occurrence: North Carolina: Nash County: 3½ miles northwest of Rockymount; St. Mary's formation;
U. S. Geological Survey; Cat. No. 166062.
Collection: U. S. National Museum.
Type: Recent.

PLIOCENE

Order DECAPODA

Family PAGURIDAE
Genus PETROCHIRUS Stimpson
Petrochirus bouvieri Rathbun

For synonymy, see under "Miocene," page 105.
Occurrence: Florida; Caloosahatchee marl.
Glades County: About 6 miles northwest of Clewiston; dredged at a
depth of 30 to 40 feet; J. C. Simpson, collector.
Collection: Florida Geological Survey.

Family XANTHIDAE
Genus MENIPPE DeHaan
Menippe nodifrons Stimpson

For synonymy, see under "Miocene," page 110.
Occurrence: Same as the preceding.
Collection: Florida Geological Survey.

Genus PANOPEUS Milne Edwards
Panopeus herbstii Milne Edwards

For synonymy, see under "Miocene," p. 111.
Occurrence: North Carolina; Waccamaw formation:

Bladen County: Walker's Bluff, Cape Fear River; one specimen; Cat. No. 166089.

Columbus County: Neill's Eddy Landing, Cape Fear River; one specimen; Cat. No. 166074.

Collection: U. S. National Museum.

Genus EURYTIUM Stimpson
Eurytium limosum (Say)

For synonymy, see under "Miocene," page 111.

Occurrence: North Carolina; Waccamaw formation:

Bladen County: Walker's Bluff, Cape Fear River; four fingers; Cat. No. 166090.

Columbus County: Neill's Eddy Landing, Cape Fear River; one immovable finger; Cat. No. 166091.

Collection: U. S. National Museum.

Family PARTHENOPIDAE
Genus PARTHENOPE Weber
Parthenope (Platylambrus) charlottensis Rathbun, n.sp.

(Plate 24, figures 31–34)

Holotype, the propodus of a left cheliped. The upper surface is four times as long as its greatest width excluding marginal spines, and bears dorsally a number of short conical spines arranged mostly in two rows, one row near the outer edge, the other just inside the middle line. On the outer margin are ten large flat spines, with a short narrow one between the seventh and the eighth (counting from the wrist); the spines are in the same plane as the upper surface; the two distal spines lack their tips, the remaining eight are nearly of a size, their axes nearly at right angles to the propodal margin, and their proximal margins a little more convex than their distal margins. On the inner margin of the palm are 21 short, triangular, blunt spines inclined obliquely upward and distad; these spines are thick and coarsely granulated below, which gives them a lumpy appearance; with a few exceptions they increase in size toward the distal end. The lower surface is nearly smooth and is a trifle narrower than the upper; its inner border consists of about 36 tubercles including those on the finger. The narrow inner surface has a few coarse scattered granules. The propodal finger is inclined strongly downward, the prehensile margin broad and triangular, having a short blunt tooth not far from the tip.

Measurements: Greatest length of upper surface of palm, 33.8 millimeters; greatest width, spines excluded, 8.2 millimeters; greatest width, spines included, 14 millimeters; length of propodus measured on lower margin to end of finger, 35 millimeters.

Relation: Closely allied to the Recent *P. (Platy.) serrata*[62] which inhabits

[62] M. J. Rathbun: *The spider crabs of America*, U. S. Nat. Mus., Bull. 129 (1925) p. 516, pls. 180, 181, 275, figs. 7–10.

the coast from Cape Hatteras to Brazil. In that species the spines of the outer margin alternate large and small, and the spines of both outer and inner margins trend strongly distad.

Occurrence: Florida: Charlotte County: Alligator Creek, Willcox; Caloosahatchee marl; U. S. Geological Survey.

Collection: U. S. National Museum; type, Cat. No. 371716.

PLEISTOCENE

Order DECAPODA

Family HOMARIDAE
Genus HOMARUS Weber
Homarus americanus Milne Edwards

1837. *Homarus americanus.* Milne Edwards, Hist. Nat. Crust., vol. 2, p. 334.
1893. *Homarus americanus.* R. Rathbun, Fisheries and Fishery Industries of U. S., sec. 1, p. 781, pl. 271.

Occurrence:
Long Island Sound, dredged three quarters of a mile off shore from Westbrook, Connecticut, by Bert Stevens, July 1, 1927; a pair of claws encrusted with *Balanus* and Recent Bryozoans.
Chaleurs Bay, New Brunswick; Leda clay (R. Chalmers, 1886).
Collections: American Museum of Natural History; Geological Commission of Canada, Ottawa.
Type: Paris Museum; Recent.

Family CALLIANASSIDAE
Genus CALLIANASSA Leach
Callianassa atlantica Rathbun

For synonymy, see under "Miocene," page 104.

Occurrence: Maryland: St. Mary's County: Wailes Bluff; Talbot formation; Frank Burns, collector (2032); one movable, one immovable finger; Cat. No. 371724.

Same locality and formation; lower bed; W. C. Mansfield, collector (8932); one movable finger; Cat. No. 371725.

Collection: U. S. National Museum.

Type: Recent.

Family CALAPPIDAE
Genus CALAPPA Weber
Calappa flammea (Herbst)

1860. *Calappa marmorata.* F. S. Holmes, Post-Pleiocene Fossils of South Carolina, p. 8, pl. 2, fig. 6.
For further synonymy, see under "Miocene," page 106.

Occurrence: South Carolina: Colleton County: Sandy beds, Wadmalaw Sound (F. S. Holmes).
Collection: Museum, College of Charleston, S. C.
Type: Not extant; Recent.

Family LEUCOSIIDAE
Genus PERSEPHONA Leach
Persephona punctata (Linnaeus)

1860. *Guia punctata.* F. S. Holmes, Post-Pleiocene Fossils of South Carolina, p. 8, pl. 2, fig. 8.

For further synonymy, see under "Miocene," page 106.

Occurrence: North Carolina: Carteret County: Open Land Project, about 10 miles northwest from Beaufort and about 6 miles from North River; Pamlico formation; May 6, 1925; W. C. Mansfield, collector (1/892); two arms; Cat. No. 371473.

South Carolina: Colleton County: Sandy beds, Wadmalaw Sound (F. S. Holmes).

Collection: U. S. National Museum; Museum, College of Charleston, S. C.

Type: Recent.

Family PORTUNIDAE
Genus CALLINECTES Stimpson
Callinectes sapidus Rathbun

1860. *Lupa dicantha.* F. S. Holmes, Post-Pleiocene Fossils of South Carolina, p. 9.

1891. *Callinectes hastatus.* R. P. W[hitfield], Science, vol. 18, no. 460, p. 300.

1906. *Callinectes sapidus.* W. B. Clark, Md. Geol. Survey, pleistocene, p. 172, pl. 41, figs. 1 and 2 (not 3).

For further synonymy, see under "Miocene," page 107.

Occurrence:

Massachusetts: Sankaty Head, Nantucket; J. Howard Wilson, collector.

New Jersey: Hudson River tunnel (R. P. Whitfield).

New Jersey; Cape May formation: H. G. Richards, collector: Ocean County: Seaside Heights, one chela, Cat. No. 371929; Beach Arlington, one finger, Cat. No. 371931. Cape May County: Stone Harbor, one finger, Cat. No. 371930; Two Mile Beach, 20 fingers, Cat. Nos. 371258, 371933–371936.

Maryland: St. Mary's County; Wailes Bluff; Talbot formation; Frank Burns, collector (2032); two fingers; Cat. No. 146701.

Maryland: Wailes Bluff; lower bed; Talbot formation; W. C. Mansfield, collector (8932); fragments of four fingers; Cat. No. 371727.

Maryland: Wailes Bluff; left bank of Potomac River, half to three quarters of a mile above the residence of the late Col. Wailes; taken from the lower bed, or the bed below the oyster bed; Talbot formation; June 26, 1925; L. W. Stephenson, W. C. Mansfield, and W. P. Popenoe, collectors (1/902); two fingers; Cat. No. 371726.

Maryland: Near mouth of Choptank River, Cook Point, Dorchester County; Talbot formation (W. B. Clark).

Maryland: Ocean City, Worcester County; H. G. Richards, collector; three chelae; Cat. No. 371932.

Virginia: Northampton County: Broadwater; Ray Phillips, collector; one large specimen; Cat. No. 371729.

North Carolina: Carteret County: Core Creek Canal, north of Beaufort; one finger; Cat. No. 371263.

South Carolina: Colleton County: Sandy beds, Wadmalaw Sound (F. S. Holmes).

Collection: U. S. National Museum, Maryland Geological Survey, Johns Hopkins University; Museum, College of Charleston, S. C.; American Museum of Natural History.

Type: Recent.

Family CANCRIDAE
Genus CANCER Linnaeus
Cancer irroratus Say

1817. *Cancer irroratus.* Say, Philadelphia Acad. Nat. Sci., Jour., vol. 1, p. 59, pl. 4, fig. 2 (part, male).

1861. *Cancer irroratus.* Hitchcock, Maine Board Agric., Sixth Ann. Rept., p. 277; marine clays near Portland.

Occurrence:

Maine: Westbrook, Cumberland County: from landslide on the Stroudwater River; Leda clay; 11 specimens, fragmentary; Charles B. Fuller, collector. The landslide was about three miles from the present coast.

The single manus in this collection is of small size and differs from typical specimens in this particular, that the upper row of granules on the outer surface is in line with the globular condyle articulating with the carpus, instead of being above the condyle.

New Jersey: Two-mile Beach; Cape May formation; H. G. Richards, collector; 27 fingers; Cat. No. 371259, 371937–371941.

Maryland: St. Mary's County: Wailes Bluff; left bank of Potomac River, half to three quarters of a mile above the residence of the late Col. Wailes. Taken from the lower bed, or the bed below the oyster bed; Talbot formation; June 26, 1925; L. W. Stephenson, W. C. Mansfield, and W. P. Popenoe, collectors (1/902); two left chelipeds, one showing the four large segments, the other the chela and carpus; Cat. No. 371710.

Maryland: Wailes Bluff; Talbot formation; Frank Burns, collector (2032); two chelae, one with carpus attached; Cat. No. 371711.

Florida: Miami Beach; H. G. Richards, collector; two fingers, returned to sender.

Collections: U. S. National Museum; Portland Society of Natural History (Charles B. Fuller collection).

Type: Not extant; Recent.

Family XANTHIDAE
Genus PANOPEUS Milne Edwards
Panopeus herbstii Milne Edwards

For synonymy, see under "Miocene," page 111.

Occurrence:

Massachusetts: Sankaty Head, Nantucket; J. Howard Wilson, collector; returned to sender.

New Jersey: Two-mile Beach; Cape May formation; H. G. Richards, collector; five fingers; Cat. Nos. 371942–371945.

Maryland: St. Mary's County: Wailes Bluff; lower bed; Talbot formation; W. C. Mansfield, collector (8932); three fingers; Cat. No. 371722.

Same locality and collector; upper bed; (8933); one finger; Cat. No. 371720.

South Carolina: Bolton Phosphate Company, Stone River; immovable finger; Cat. No. 166073.

Collection: U. S. National Museum.

Genus MENIPPE DeHaan
Menippe mercenaria (Say)

1818. *Cancer mercenaria.* Say, Philadelphia Acad. Nat. Sci., Jour., vol. 1, p. 448.

1860. *Pseudocarcinus mercenaria.* F. S. Holmes, Post-Pleiocene Fossils of South Carolina, p. 8, pl. 2, fig. 7.

1930. *Menippe mercenaria.* Rathbun, U. S. Nat. Mus., Bull. 152, p. 472, text-fig. 78, pl. 191–193.

Occurrence: South Carolina: Colleton County: Sandy beds, Wadmalaw Sound (F. S. Holmes).
Collection: Museum, College of Charleston, S. C.
Type: Not extant; Recent.

Family OCYPODIDAE
Genus OCYPODE Fabricius
Ocypode albicans Bosc

1801–1802. *Ocypoda albicans.* Bosc, Hist. Nat. Crust., vol. 1, an X, p. 196 (not pl. 4, fig. 1).

1918. *Ocypode albicans.* Rathbun, U. S. Nat. Mus., Bull. 97, p. 367, pls. 127 and 128, and synonymy.

Dorsal surface of carapace and surface of chelipeds and legs covered with a hard coating of sand. The ornamentation of the pterygostomian region, the ischium of the outer maxilliped, the sternum and abdomen and the base of the rostrum coincides with that of the Recent well-known "ghost crab."

Occurrence: Florida (probably); J. J. White collection; one large ♀; Cat. No. 371733.
Collection: U. S. National Museum.

Genus UCA Leach
Uca pugnax (Smith)

1870. *Gelasimus pugnax.* Smith, Conn. Acad. Arts and Sci., Tr., vol. 2, p. 131, pl. 2, fig. 1, pl. 4, figs. 2–2d.
1918. *Uca pugnax.* Rathbun, U. S. Nat. Mus., Bull. 97, p. 395, pl. 139, and synonymy.

Occurrence:
New Jersey: Anglesea, Cape May County; Cape May formation; H. G. Richards, collector; three chelae; Cat. No. 371946.
Delaware: Rehoboth Beach, Sussex County; H. G. Richards, collector; four leg fragments; Cat. No. 371947.
Collection: U. S. National Museum.
Type: Peabody Museum, Yale University; Recent.

Uca subcylindrica (Stimpson)

1859. *Gelasimus subcylindricus.* Stimpson, Lyc. Nat. Hist. New York, Ann., vol. 7, p. 63.
1918. *Uca subcylindrica.* Rathbun, U. S. Nat. Mus., Bull. 97, p. 419, pl. 155, pl. 160, fig. 5, and synonymy.

Occurrence: Texas: Brooks County: 7.3 miles north of Encino post office, in roadside caliche pit; A. C. Trowbridge, collector (9095); 16 major palms with more or less of the fixed finger attached, and 6 major movable fingers; Cat. No. 371712.
Collection: U. S. National Museum.
Cotypes: Museum of Comparative Zoology; Recent.

Family MAJIDAE
Genus HYAS Leach
Hyas araneus (Linnaeus)

1758. *Cancer araneus.* Linnaeus, Syst. Nat., ed. 10, vol. 1, p. 628.
1925. *Hyas araneus.* Rathbun, U. S. Nat. Mus., Bull. 129, p. 253, text-figs. 91 and 92, pls. 92 and 93, and synonymy.

Occurrence: Maine: Westbrook, Cumberland County: Landslide on the Stroudwater River; one specimen showing the propodus and dactylus of an ambulatory leg. Landslide at Cumberland Mills, 1868; one specimen of chela and wrist. Leda clay, Pleistocene.
Collection: Portland Society of Natural History (Charles B. Fuller collection).
Type: Not extant; Recent.

Libinia emarginata Leach

1815. *Libinia emarginata.* Leach, Zool. Misc., vol. 2, p. 130, pl. 108.
1925. *Libinia emarginata.* Rathbun, U. S. Nat. Mus., Bull. 129, p. 311, text-figs. 103 and 104, pl. 110–113.

Occurrence: New Jersey: Cape May County: Cape May formation; Two Mile Beach, one finger, Cat. No. 371948; Cape May, one finger tip, Cat. No. 371949.
Collection: U. S. National Museum.
Type: British Museum; Recent.

Libinia dubia Milne Edwards

1834. *Libinia dubia.* Milne Edwards, Hist. Nat. Crust., vol. 1, p. 300, pl. 14 bis, fig. 2.

1925. *Libinia dubia.* Rathbun, U. S. Nat. Mus., Bull. 129, p. 313, text-fig. 105, pl. 114, 115, 122, fig. 1.

Occurrence: New Jersey: Two Mile Beach, Cape May County; Cape May formation; eight fingers; Cat. Nos. 371950-371952.

Collection: U. S. National Museum.

Type: Paris Museum; Recent.

Order STOMATOPODA

Family CHLORIDELLIDAE

Genus CHLORIDELLA Miers

Chloridella empusa (Say)

1818. *Squilla empusa.* Say, Philadelphia Acad. Nat. Sci., Jour., vol. 1, p. 250.

1844. *Squilla empusa.* DeKay, Nat. Hist. New York, pt. 6, Crust., p. 32, pl. 13, fig. 54.

1905. *Chloridella empusa.* Rathbun, Boston Soc. Nat. Hist., Occas. Pap., vol. 7, p. 29.

Occurrence: Maryland: St. Mary's County:

Wailes Bluff; left bank of Potomac River, half to three-quarters of a mile above the residence of the late Col. Wailes; lower bed, or the bed below the oyster bed; Talbot formation; June 26, 1925; L. W. Stephenson, W. C. Mansfield, and W. P. Popenoe, collectors (1/902); one telson; Cat. No. 371732.

Wailes Bluff; lower bed; Talbot formation; W. C. Mansfield, collector (8932); one terminal article of second thoracic appendage; Cat. No. 371731.

Collection: U. S. National Museum.

Type: Philadelphia Academy of Natural Sciences; Recent.

BIBLIOGRAPHY

Adkins, Walter Scott
   1918. The Weno and Pawpaw formations of the Texas Comanchean. Univ. Texas, Bull. 1856, p. 62.
   1928. Handbook of Cretaceous fossils. Univ. Texas, Bull. 2838, p. 83.

Ammon, Ludwig von
   1882. Ein Beitrag zur Kenntniss der vorweltlichen Asseln. Sitzungsb. math. phys. Cl. k. b. Akad. Wiss. München, vol. 12, p. 519, pls. 1–4.

Bell, Thomas
   1850. In F. Dixon, Geology and Fossils of the Tertiary and Cretaceous formations of Sussex, pl. 38, fig. 2.
   1863. A monograph of the fossil malacostracous Crustacea of Great Britain. Part II. Crustacea of the Gault and Greensand, p. 21, pl. 4, fig. 9–11.

Bittner, Alexander
   1875. Die Brachyuren des Vicentinischen Tertiärgebirges. Denkschr. Akad. d. Wissensch., Wien, vol. 34, p. 75 [15], pl. 1, figs. 9 and 10.

Bosc, Louis Augustin Guillaume
   1801–1802. Histoire Naturelle des Crustacés, contenant leur description et leurs moeurs, vol. 1, an X, p. 196.

Carter, James
   1898. A contribution to the palaeontology of the decapod Crustacea of England. Geol. Soc. London, Quart. Jour., vol. 54, pl. 1, fig. 1.

Clark, William Bullock
   1906. Systematic paleontology, Pleistocene. Md. Geol. Surv., Pleistocene, p. 172–174, pl. 41, figs. 1, 2.

Cooke, Charles Wythe and Stuart Mossom
   1929. The Geology of Florida. Florida Geol. Surv., 20th Ann. Rept., 1927–1928, p. 116.

Credner, Hermann
   1870. Die Kreide von New Jersey. Deutsch. geol. Ges., Zeitschr., vol. 22, p. 241.

Cushman, Joseph Augustine
   1905. Fossil crabs of the Gay Head Miocene. Am. Nat., vol. 39, p. 381–390.

Davis, William Thompson and Leng, Charles William
   1927. Cretaceous fossils from Staten Island. Staten Island Inst. Arts and Sci., Pr., vol. 4, p. 47, pls. 2, 3 (upper).

Dekay, James Ellsworth
   1844. Nat. Hist. N. Y., pt. 6, Crustacea, p. 32, pl. 13, fig. 54.

Desmarest, Anselme-Gaëtan
   1822. In Brongniart and Desmarest, Histoire naturelle des Crustacés fossiles. Les Crustacés proprement dits, p. 130, pl. 7, figs. 3, 4. Paris.

Edwards, Alphonse Milne
   1862–1865. Monographie des Crustacés de la famille des Cancériens. Ann. Sci. Nat., Zool., sér. 4, vol. 18 (1862) p. 71, pl. 10, fig. 2–2d; sér. 4, vol. 20 (1862) pl. 9, fig.

1–1d; sér. 5, vol. 1 (1864) p. 44; sér. 5, vol. 3 (1865) pl. 9, fig. 1c; p. 332, pl. 10, fig. 1, 1a.

1879. Isopode gigantesque des grandes profondeurs de la mer. Compt. Rend., vol. 88, p. 21.

1879. Note sur quelques Crustacés fossiles appartenant au groupe des Macrophthalmiens. Bull. Soc. Philom., ser. 7, vol. 3, p. 117.

Edwards, Henri Milne

1834–1837. Histoire Naturelle des Crustacés, comprenant l'anatomie, la physiologie et la classification de ces animaux, vol. 1, p. 300, 402, pl. 14, bis., fig. 2; vol. 2, p. 334.

Fabricius, Johann Christian

1798. Supplementum Entomologiae Systematicae, p. 371.

Forskål, Peter

1775. Descriptiones Animalium quae in itinere orientali observavit P. Forskål, p. 90.

Fritsch, Antonin Jan and Kafka, Josef

1887. Die Crustaceen d. böhm. Kreideformation, p. 40.

Gabb, William More

1864. Description of the Cretaceous fossils. Calif. Geol. Surv., Pal., vol. 1, sect. 4, p. 57, pl. 9, fig. 1a, b, c.

Gibbes, Lewis R.

1850. On the Carcinological collections of the cabinets of Natural History in the United States. Am. Assoc. Adv. Sci., Pr., vol. 3, p. 178 [14].

Glaessner, Martin F.

1929. Fossilium Catalogus, vol. 1, pt. 41, p. 395.

Hansen, Hans Jacob

1895. Isopoden, Cumaceen und Stomatopoden der Plankton-Exped. Ergebnisse der Plankton-Expedition der Humboldt-Stiftung, Bd. II, p. 65.

Harris, Gilbert Dennison

1894. The Tertiary geology of southern Arkansas. Ark. Geol. Surv., Ann. Rept. 1892, vol. 2, p. 36, pl. 1, fig. 2a, b.

Hay, William Perry and Shore, Clarence Albert

1918. The Decapod Crustaceans of Beaufort, N. C. and the surrounding region. Bur. Fisheries, Bull., vol. 35, 1915–1916, p. 423, pl. 32, fig. 9, and synonymy.

Henderson, John Robertson

1888. Report on the Anomura collected by H. M. S. Challenger during the years 1873–76. Challenger report, Zool., vol. 27, p. 34.

Herbst, Johann Friedrich Wilhelm

1794. Versuch einer Naturgeschichte der Krabben und Krebse nebst einer systematischen beschreibung ihrer verschiedenen arten, vol. 2, p. 161, pl. 40, fig. 2.

Hill, Robert Thomas

1901. Geography and geology of the Black and Grand prairies, Texas. U. S. Geol. Surv., Ann. Rept. 21, pt. 7, p. 302.

Hitchcock, Charles Henry

1861. General report upon the geology of Maine. Maine Bd. Agric., 6th Ann. Rept., p. 277.

Holmes, Francis S.

1860. Post-Pleiocene Fossils of South Carolina, p. 8, pl. 2, figs. 6, 7, 8, p. 9.

Johnson, Charles Willison

1905. Annotated list of the types of invertebrate Cretaceous fossils in the collection of the Academy of Natural Sciences, Philadelphia. Philadelphia Acad. Nat. Sci., Pr., vol. 57, p. 28.

Kafka, Josef. See Fritsch.

Leach, William Elford

1815. Zoological Miscellany, vol. 2, p. 130, pl. 108.

Leng, Charles William. See Davis.

Linnaeus, Carolus

1758. Systema Naturae, ed. 10, vol. 1, p. 628, 630 (part).

Lörenthey, Emerich

1898. Beiträge zur Decapodenfauna des ungarischen Tertiärs. Természetrajzi Füzetek, vol. 21, p. 142, pl. 11, figs. 2a–2e, 3a, 3b.

Mantell, Gideon Algernon

1822. The fossils of the South Downs, or Illustrations of the Geology of Sussex. London.

Maury, Carlotta Joaquina

1930. O Cretaceo da Parahyba do Norte. Servico Geologico Mineralogico do Brasil, Monog. 8, p. 111, pl. 4, figs. 1 and 2.

McCoy, Frederick

1849. On the classification of some British fossil Crustacea with notices of new forms in the University Collection at Cambridge. Ann. Mag. Nat. Hist., ser. 2, vol. 4, p. 175, text figures.

1854. On some new Cretaceous Crustacea. Ann. Mag. Nat. Hist., ser. 2, vol. 14, p. 118, pl. 4, fig. 3.

Morton, Samuel George

1830. Synopsis of the organic remains of the ferruginous sand formation of the United States, with geological remarks. Am. Jour. Sci., vol. 17, p. 287.

Mossom, Stuart. See Cooke.

Ortmann, Arnold Edward

1897. On a new species of the palinurid genus Linuparus found in the Upper Cretaceous of Dakota. Am. Jour. Sci., ser. 4, vol. 4, p. 290–296.

Packard, Alpheus Spring, Jr.

1900. A new fossil crab from the Miocene greensand bed of Gay Head, Marthas Vineyard, with remarks on the phylogeny of the genus Cancer. Am. Acad. Arts, Sci., Pr., vol. 36, p. 1–9.

1900. A partial phylogeny of the genus Cancer. Am. Assoc. Adv. Sci., Pr., vol. 49, p. 239.

Pelseneer, Paul

1886. Notice sur les Crustacés décapodes du Maestrichtien du Limbourg. Mus. Roy. Hist. Nat. Belgique, Bull., vol. 4, p. 170 [10], fig. 6.

Pilsbry, Henry Augustus

1900. Crustacea of the Cretaceous formation of New Jersey. Philadelphia Acad. Nat. Sci., Pr., vol. 53, p. 111–118.

1916. Arthropoda *in* Upper Cretaceous, Md. Geol. Surv., p. 361–370.

1916. Systematic Paleontology of the Upper Cretaceous deposits of Maryland. (Arthropoda). Md. Geol. Survey, Upper Cretaceous, p. 361, pl. 10, figs. 1–4, 8, 9.

Rathbun, Mary Jane

1896. The genus Callinectes. U. S. Nat. Mus., Pr., vol. 18, p. 352, pls. 12, 24. fig. 1, 25, fig. 1, 26, fig. 1, 27, fig. 1.

1901. The Brachyura and Macrura of Porto Rico. U. S. Fish Commission for 1900, Bull., vol. 20, pt. 2, p. 84, pl. 2, and synonymy.

1905. Fauna of New England, List of the Crustacea. Boston Soc. Nat. Hist., Occ. Pap., vol. 7, p. 29.

1917. New species of South Dakota Cretaceous crabs. U. S. Nat. Mus., Pr., vol. 52, p. 385–391.

1918. The Grapsoid Crabs of America. U. S. Nat. Mus., Bull. 97, p. 367, pls. 127, 128, p. 395, pl. 139, p. 419, pls. 155, 160, fig. 5.

1919. Decapod crustaceans from the Panama region. U. S. Nat. Mus., Bull. 103 (1918) not issued until Jan., 1919, p. 123–184.

1919. West Indian Tertiary decapod crustaceans. Carnegie Inst. Washington, Pub. 291, p. 157–184, 9 plates.

1923. Decapod crustaceans from the Upper Cretaceous of North Carolina. N. C. Geol. Surv., vol. 5, p. 407, pl. 102, figs. 1–3 (p. 403–408).

1925. The Spider Crabs of America. U. S. Nat. Mus., Bull. 129, p. 253, text figs. 91, 92, pls. 92, 93, p. 311, text figs. 103, 104, pl. 110–113, p. 313, text figs. 105, 106, pls. 114, 115, 122, fig. 1, p. 449, pl. 160, 161, p. 516, pl. 180, 181, 275, figs. 7–10.

1925. *In* Hull, J. P. D.: Guide notes on the Midway in southwestern Arkansas. Am. Assoc. Petr. Geol., Bull., vol. 9, no. 1, p. 168 (p. 167–170).

1926. The fauna of the Ripley formation on Coon Creek, Tennessee. U. S. Geol. Surv., Prof. Pap. 137, p. 185, pl. 63, figs. 1–6, 8–11, p. 187, pl. 66 (p. 184–191).

1926. The fossil stalk-eyed crustacea of the Pacific slope of North America. U. S. Nat. Mus., Bull. 138.

1928. Two new crabs from the Eocene of Texas. U. S. Nat. Mus., Pr., vol. 73, art. 6, 6 pages, 3 plates.

1929. A new crab from the Eocene of Florida. U. S. Nat. Mus., Pr., vol. 75, art. 15, 4 pages, 3 plates.

1930. The Cancroid Crabs of America of the Families Euryalidae, Portunidae, Atelecyclidae, Cancridae, and Xanthidae. U. S. Nat. Mus., Bull. 152, p. 37, text figs. 6, 7, pl. 14, p. 84, pl. 41, p. 182, fig. 30, p. 335, text-figs. 52, 53, pl. 156, 157, and synonymy, p. 348, pl. 161, p. 423, pl. 176, figs. 1, 2, and synonymy, p. 472, text fig. 78, pl. 191–193, p. 478, pl. 198, fig. 1, p. 479, pl. 198, fig. 3, 199.

1931. A new fossil palinurid from Staten Island. Staten Island Inst. Arts and Sci., Pr., vol. 5, p. 161–162.

Rathbun, Richard

1893. Fisheries and Fishery Industries of United States, sect. 1, p. 781, pl. 271.

Reed, Frederick Richard Cowper

1911. New Crustacea from the lower Greensand of the Isle of Wight. Geol. Mag., n.s., Dec. 5, vol. 8, 116, pl. 7, fig. 2.

Reeside, John Bernard

1927. The Cephalopods of the Eagle sandstone and related formations in the western interior of the United States. U. S. Geol. Surv., Prof. Pap. 151.

Reuss, August Emanuel

1859. Zur Kenntniss fossiler Krabben. Denksch. k. Akad. Wiss. math. natur. Cl., vol. 17, p. 4, pl. 2, figs. 1–3.

Roemer, Friedrich Adolph

1887. Graptocarcinus texanus, ein Brachyure aus der oberen Kreide von Texas. Neues Jahrb. Min., Geol., Pal., vol. 1, p. 173.

Say, Thomas
1817–1818. An account of the crustacea of the United States. Philadelphia Acad. Nat. Sci., Jour., vol. 1, p. 59, pl. 4, fig. 2, p. 57–458.

Schlüter, Clemens
1862. Die Macruren Decapoden der Senon- und Cenomanbildungen Westphalens. Zeitschr. d. deutschen Geol. Ges., vol. 14, pl. 11, fig. 5.

Schuchert, Charles
1905. Catalogue of the type specimens of fossil invertebrates in the Department of Geology. U. S. Nat. Mus., Bull. 53, p. 484.

Smith, Sidney Irving
1870. Notes on American Crustacea. No. 1. Ocypodoidea. Conn. Acad. Arts and Sci., Tr., vol. 2, p. 131, pl. 2, fig. 1, pl. 4, figs. 2–2b.
1873. Report upon the Invertebrate Animals of Vineyard Sound and adjacent waters, with an account of the physical features of the region. U. S. Commr. Fish and Fisheries, Rept. for 1871–1872, pt. 1, p. 549 [255], pl. 2, fig. 8.

Stenzel, Henryk Bronislaw
1934. Decapod Crustaceans from the Middle Eocene of Texas. Jour. Pal., vol. 8, no. 1, p. 41, pl. 6, figs. 2a, b, 3, p. 49, pl. 7, figs. 1a–c, p. 51, pl. 7, figs. a, b, p. 53, pl. 7, figs. 3a–f, p. 55, pl. 7, figs. 4a, b.

Stimpson, William
1859. Notes on North American Crustacea, No. 1. N. Y. Lyc. Nat. Hist., Ann., vol. 7, p. 53 (7), p. 63.
1860. Notes on North American Crustacea, in the Museum of the Smithsonian Institution. No. II. N. Y. Lyc. Nat. Hist., Ann., vol. 7, p. 225 [97], pl. 3, fig. 5.
1863. On the fossil crab of Gay Head (Marthas Vineyard, Mass.). Boston Jour. Nat. Hist., vol. 7, p. 583–589.

Stolíczka, Ferdinand
1871. Observations on fossil crabs from Tertiary deposits in Sind and Kutch. Geol. Survey India, Mem., Palaeontol. Indica, ser. 7, No. 14, 1871, vol. 1, part 1, pl. 3, figs. 2c, 2d.

Toula, Franz
1911. Die jungtertiäre Fauna von Gatun am Panamakanal. Jahrb. der k. k. Geolog. Reichsanstalt, Wien, vol. 61, p. 511 (25), pl. 30 (1), fig. 13.

Weber, Fridericus
1795. Nomenclator entomologicus, p. 92.

Weller, Stuart
1905. The fauna of the Cliffwood, New Jersey, clays. N. J. Geol. Surv., Ann. Rept. for 1904, p. 136, 139, 141, pl. 15, figs. 4–6; Jour. Geol., vol. 13, p. 328, figs. 4–6.
1907. A report on the Cretaceous paleontology of New Jersey, based upon the stratigraphic studies of George N. Knapp. N. J. Geol. Surv., Pal. ser., vol. 4, p. 846, pl. 110, figs. 12–15, p. 848, pl. 110, figs. 16, 17 (p. 843–853), Atlas, pl. 111, figs. 16–19.

White, Charles Abiathar
1881. Descriptions of new invertebrate fossils from the Mesozoic and Cenozoic rocks of Arkansas, Wyoming, Colorado, and Utah. U. S. Nat. Mus., Pr., vol. 3, 1880 (1881) p. 161; vol. 4 (1881) p. 137, pl. 1, figs. 10 and 11.
1882. On certain Cretaceous fossils from Arkansas and Colorado. U. S. Nat. Mus., Pr., vol. 4, p. 131, pl. 1, figs. 10, 11.

Whiteaves, Joseph Frederick
1885. Report on the invertebrata of the Laramie and Cretaceous rocks of the vicinity of the Bow and Belly rivers and adjacent localities in the Northwest Territory. Can. Geol. Surv., Contr. Can. Pal., vol. 1, pt. 1, p. 87, pl. 11.

1885. Note on a decapod crustacean from the Upper Cretaceous of Highwood River, Alberta, Northwest Territory. Royal Soc. Can., Tr., vol. 2, sect. 4, p. 237–238.

1895. On some fossils from the Nanaimo group of the Vancouver Cretaceous. Royal Soc. Can., Pr., Tr., ser. 2, vol. 1, p. 132, 133.

1903. On some additional fossils from the Vancouver Cretaceous, with a revised list of the species therefrom. Can. Geol. Surv., Mesozoic fossils, vol. 1, pt. 5, p. 323, 325.

Whitfield, Robert Parr

1880. *In* C. A. White: Contributions to paleontology. U. S. Geol. Surv. Terr. for 1878, 12th Ann. Rept., p. 37, pl. 16, figs. 1a–c, pl. 17, fig. 1a.

1891. The common edible crab found fossil in the Hudson River tunnel. Science, vol. 18, no. 460, p. 300.

Whitney, Francis Luther

1913. Fauna of the Buda Limestone. Texas Acad. Sci., Tr., 1910–1912, vol. 12, p. 27, pl. 13, figs. 1, 2, 3.

Winton, Will McClain

1925. The geology of Denton County. Texas Univ., Bull. 2544, p. 71, pl. 15, fig. 2.

Withers, Thomas Henry

1922. On a new brachyurous Crustacean from the Upper Cretaceous of Jamaica. Ann. Mag. Nat. Hist., ser. 9, vol. 10, pls. 16 and 17.

Woods, Henry

1922. *In* Bosworth, Geology of northwestern Peru, p. 115, pl. 17, figs. 7–10.

1925–1926. A monograph of the fossil macrurous Crustacea of England. Palaeont. Soc. London, Mem., vol. 77 (1923) p. 26, 39; vol. 78 (1924) pl. 10, fig. 6.

Woodward, Henry

1866. On the oldest known British Crab (*Palæinachus longipes*) from the Forest Marble, Malmesbury, Wilts. Geol. Soc. London, Quart. Jour., vol. 22, p. 592, pl. 26, fig. 18.

1870. Contributions to British fossil Crustacea. Geol. Mag., vol. 7, p. 496, pl. 22, figs. 3–6.

1900. Further note on podophthalmous crustaceans from the Upper Cretaceous formation of British Columbia. Geol. Mag., n. s., dec. 4, vol. 7, p. 392–401, 433–435.

EXPLANATION OF PLATES

PLATE 1—CRUSTACEA FROM THE CRETACEOUS

FIGURES 1–12.—*Enoploclytia tumimanus* Rathbun, n.sp. From Selma chalk in vicinity of Prairie Creek, Allenton and Pine Barren section, Wilcox County, Alabama; L. C. Johnson; Sec. 32 and 34, T. 12 S., R. 10 E.; Cat. No.*73799. [*See* page 18.]

1–4.—Upper, lower, inner, and outer views of left arm (264), × 1.44.   5–7.—Fragments of fingers, showing teeth (264), × 1.44.   8, 9.—Dorsal view and right profile of largest carapace (284), × 1.08.   10, 11.—Dorsal view and right profile of holotype carapace (284), × 1.08.   12.—Dorsal view of smallest carapace (284), × 1.08.

* Unless otherwise stated, the catalogue numbers are those of the United States National Museum. Numbers in parenthesis indicate those used by senders.

PLATE 1

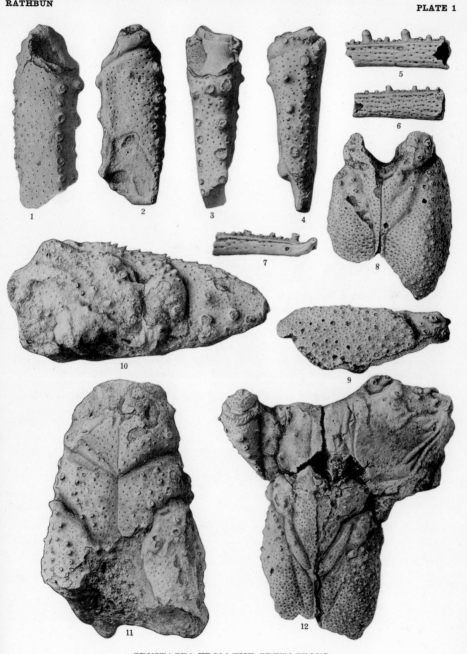

CRUSTACEA FROM THE CRETACEOUS

CRUSTACEA FROM THE CRETACEOUS

PLATE 2—CRUSTACEA FROM THE CRETACEOUS

FIGURES 1–5.—*Enoploclytia tumimanus* Rathbun, n.sp.   Inner, outer, and upper views of left palm and lower and upper views of right arm-wrist (264), × 1.08; from same lot as Plate 1.   [*See* page 18.]

FIGURE 6.—*Enoploclytia* (?) sp.   Convex fragment, Cat. No. 73842, × 1.44.   [*See* page 20.]

FIGURES 7–13.—*Hoploparia dentonensis* Rathbun, n.sp.   From Denton clay, Grayson County, Texas; W. S. Adkins, University of Texas.   [*See* page 26.]
7, 8.—Dorsal view and left profile of abdomen (182), × 1.44.   9, 10.—Lower (× 2.89) and distal (× 4.33) views of right palm, holotype (210).   11.—Lower view of right palm, paratype (210), × 2.89.   12, 13.—Dorsal view and right profile of carapace (182), × 2.16.

FIGURE 14.—*Palaeastacus selmaensis* Rathbun, n.sp.   Left wrist, upper (distal end forward), holotype, Cat. No. 73848, × .72; from Selma chalk, Prairie Creek and Allenton, Alabama.   [*See* page 24.]

FIGURES 15–21.—*Palaeastacus kimzeyi* Rathbun, n.sp.   [*See* page 23.]
15.—Piece of carapace, Cat. No. 73841, × 1.08; from base of Wolfe City sand, upper Taylor marl, about 3 miles southwest of Farmersville, Collin County, Texas. 16.—Upper view of left chela, Cat. No. 73841, × 1.08; same place as no. 15.   17–20.— Upper, outer, inner, and distal views of right manus, holotype, Cat. No. 73797, × 1.08; same place as No. 15.   21.—Outer view of right chela, Cat. No. 73841, × 1.08; same place as No. 15.

PLATE 3—CRUSTACEA FROM THE CRETACEOUS

FIGURES 1–3.—*Petrochirus taylori* Rathbun, n.sp.   Tip of left fixed finger, holotype, cross section (inner surface below) and prehensile and outer views, × 2.16, Cat. No. 73826; from base of Wolfe City sand, upper Taylor marl, 3 miles southwest of Farmersville, Collin County, Texas.   [*See* page 40.]

FIGURES 4–6.—*Ischnodactylus texanus* Rathbun, n.sp.   Texas.   [*See* page 27.]

4–5.—Outer and distal views of right propodus of cheliped (proximal end broken off) × 2.89; W. S. Adkins (241), University of Texas; from Pawpaw clay in Northern Tarrant County at Blue Mound, 1½ miles south of Haslet station.   6.—Outer view of holotype, right propodus of cheliped, × 2.89; W. S. Adkins (1142), University of Texas; from basal 2 feet of Denton clay in Grayson County, 2½ miles north of Denison.

FIGURES 7–9.—*Palaeastacus walkeri* (Whitfield).   Inner, outer, and upper views of right carpus and chela of plastotype, × .72, Cat. No. 8360, Cretaceous (formation unknown); from San Antonio, Bexar County, Texas.   [*See* page 21.]

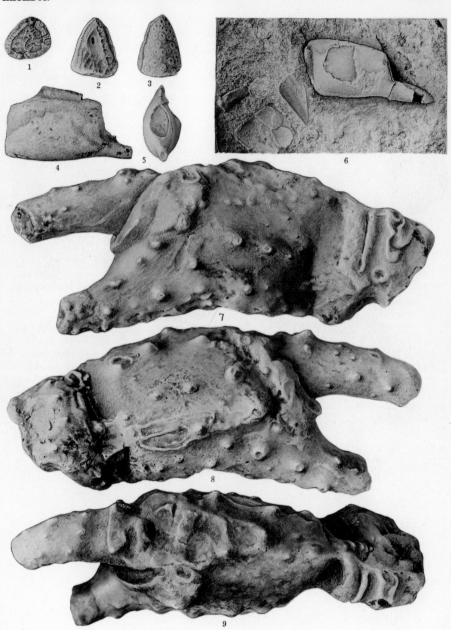

CRUSTACEA FROM THE CRETACEOUS

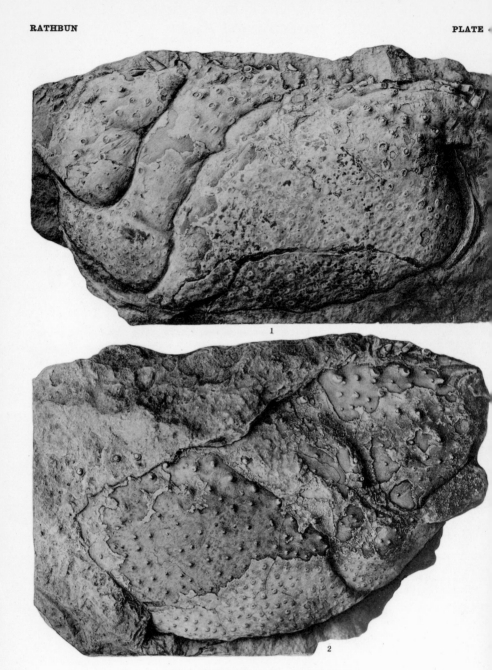

1

2

CRUSTACEA FROM THE CRETACEOUS

PLATE 4—CRUSTACEA FROM THE CRETACEOUS

FIGURES 1, 2.—*Palaeastacus walkeri* (Whitfield). Left and right sides of carapace, × .72; W. S. Adkins (201), University of Texas; from basalmost stratum of Weno, in Tarrant County, $2\frac{1}{2}$ miles southeast of Fort Worth, Texas. [*See* page 21.]

PLATE 5—CRUSTACEA FROM THE CRETACEOUS

FIGURES 1-5.—*Palaeastacus walkeri* (Whitfield). [*See* page 21.]

1-3.—Lower, outer, and inner view of left chela, lacking part of manus, × .72; University of Texas; from Buda limestone, at Shoal Creek, 29th Street, Austin, Travis County, Texas. 4.—Outer view of merus, carpus, and manus of left cheliped. × .72; W. S. Adkins, University of Texas; Fort Worth limestone, one mile north of Georgetown, cliffs on Georgetown-Belton road, Williamson County, Texas. 5.— Cross-section of carpus of plastotype, × .72 (*See* Pl. 3, figs. 7-9).

FIGURES 6-9.—*Nephrops americanus* Rathbun, n.sp. Lower view of larger right movable finger, upper view of smaller right movable finger, and upper and lower views of left immovable finger, × 2.16; W. S. Adkins, University of Texas; from Pawpaw clay, in Tarrant County, 4 miles southwest of Fort Worth, half a mile south of Baptist Seminary. [*See* page 28.]

FIGURES 10, 11.—*Hoploparia gabbi* Pilsbry. [*See* page 24.]

10.—Upper view of proximal inner part of right manus, × 7.2, Cat. No. 4692, Philadelphia Academy; from Merchantville clay marl, Monmouth County, New Jersey. 11.—Outer view of left wrist and proximal end of palm, × 1.44, Cat. No. 4691, Philadelphia Academy; from Matawan formation, deep cut of the Chesapeake and Delaware Canal.

FIGURE 12.—*Eryma stantoni* Rathbun, n.sp. A pair of chela, × 1.08, Cat. No. 73790; from the Ripley formation, Chattahoochee River, 12 miles above Eufaula, Alabama. [*See* page 21.]

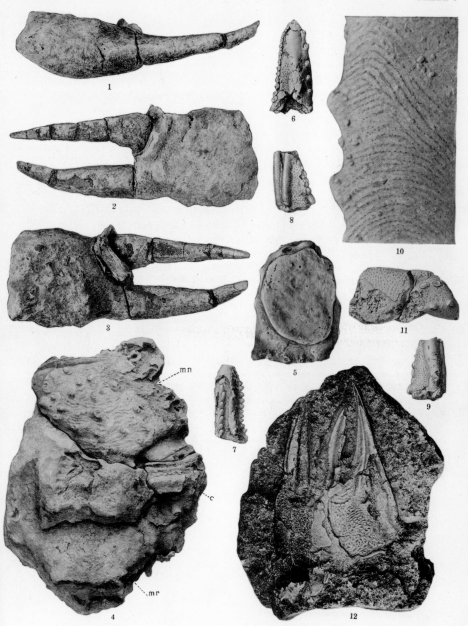

CRUSTACEA FROM THE CRETACEOUS

CRUSTACEA FROM THE CRETACEOUS

PLATE 6—CRUSTACEA FROM THE CRETACEOUS

FIGURES 1–6.—*Hoploparia blossomana* Rathbun, n.sp. From Blossom sand, about a quarter of a mile west of Detroit, Red River County, Texas, Cat. No. 73829. [*See* page 26.]

1–5.—Lower, inner, upper, and outer views and cross-section of proximal end of left manus, × 1.44. 6.—Proximal inner part of upper surface of left manus, × 7.2.

FIGURES 7, 8.—*Enoploclytia wenoensis* Rathbun, n.sp. Right profile and dorsal view of abdomen, × 1.44; W. S. Adkins, University of Texas; from Weno formation, at Gainesville, Cooke County, Texas, in brickyard pit. [*See* page 20.]

FIGURES 9–11.—*Paguristes ouachitensis* Rathbun, n.sp. Outer, lower, and distal views of left palm, × 2.16, Cat. No. 73828; from Nacatoch sand at high bluff on Ouachita River, 1.5 miles above Arkadelphia, Clark County, Arkansas, from lower masses at base of bluff. [*See* page 39.]

FIGURES 12–16.—*Callianassa cretacea* Rathbun, n.sp. [*See* page 30.]

12–15.—Inner, lower, upper, and distal views of right manus, holotype, × 2.16; W. S. Adkins (284), University of Texas; from Denton clay, southeast of Haslet and east of Blue Mound. 16.—Dorsal view of segments 3–6 of abdomen, × 1.44; W. S. Adkins (209), University of Texas; from Pawpaw clay, 4½ miles southeast of Fort Worth, a quarter of a mile south of I. G. N. Railway bridge across Sycamore Creek.

FIGURES 17–19.—*Callianassa oktibbehana* Rathbun, n.sp. Upper, outer, and inner views of right movable finger, × 2.89, Cat. No. 73825; from Oktibbeha tongue of Selma chalk, in gullies on campus of Agricultural and Mechanical College, Oktibbeha County, Mississippi. [*See* page 33.]

FIGURE 20.—*Hoploparia tarrantensis* Rathbun, n.sp. Side view of abdomen tipped a little to right to show telson, × 2.16; W. S. Adkins (284), University of Texas; from Denton clay, at Blue Mound, near Haslet, Tarrant County, Texas. [*See* page 27.]

PLATE 7—CRUSTACEA FROM THE CRETACEOUS

FIGURES 1–5.—*Callianassa aquilae* Rathbun, n.sp. Eagle Ford formation. [*See* page 31.]

1, 2.—Left profile and counterpart of holotype, × 1.44, Cat. No. 73786; from 1½ miles northeast of Sherman Junction, Grayson County, Texas, in public road ditch near base of north-facing slope of branch. 3.—Carapace and chela, × 2.16, Cat. No. 73785; from Sec. 3, T. 11 N., R. 8 W., Natchitoches Parish, in well of Amerada Petroleum Company, Wafer No. 1, depth 3165–3168 feet. 4, 5.—Portion of animal and appendages, and counterpart of the same, × 2.16, Cat. No. 73784; from Sec. 5, T. 13 N., R. 9 W., Red River Parish, in well of Amerada Petroleum Company; Long Bell No. 1, depth 2893–2903 feet.

FIGURES 6–11.—*Callianassa pilsbryi* Rathbun, n.sp. Outer view of right manus, holotype, × 1.44; outer view of left manus, × 1.44; outer and inner views of left wrist, × 1.44; inner and outer views of fixed finger, × 2.16; Cat. No. 73789; from Ripley formation, at Frisco Railroad bridge (No. 5710), 2½ miles northwest of Blue Springs, Union County, Mississippi. [*See* page 32.]

FIGURES 12–15.—*Callianassa valida* Rathbun, n.sp. Inner, outer, upper, and lower views of propodus of left cheliped, × 2.89; W. S. Adkins (210), University of Texas; from Denton clay, 2 miles north of Denison, Grayson County, Texas, half a mile east of Kde type-locality of south side St. L. S. F. Railway track. [*See* page 33.]

CRUSTACEA FROM THE CRETACEOUS

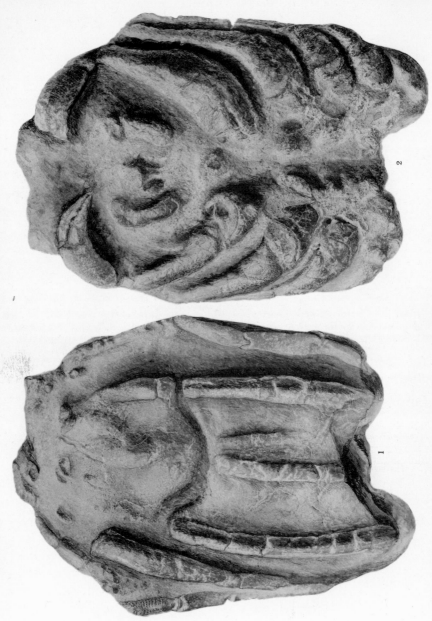

CRUSTACEA FROM THE CRETACEOUS

PLATE 8—CRUSTACEA FROM THE CRETACEOUS

FIGURES 1, 2.—*Linuparus kleinfelderi* Rathbun. Dorsal view of carapace and lower view showing appendages, × 1.01, Cat. No. 74474; from Merchantville clay marl, Matawan formation, at Fort Wadsworth, Staten Island, New York; holotype in Staten Island Museum, plastotype in U. S. National Museum. [*See* page 35.]

PLATE 9—CRUSTACEA FROM THE CRETACEOUS

FIGURES 1, 2.—*Linuparus kleinfelderi* Rathbun.   Left profile showing appendages and right profile, × 1.01.   Same specimen as in Plate 8.   [*See* page 35.]

FIGURE 3.—*Actaea cretacea* Rathbun, n.sp.   Outer view of propodus of right cheliped, × 3.61; W. S. Adkins (209), University of Texas; in Pawpaw clay, Tarrant County, Texas, 4½ miles southeast of Fort Worth, a quarter of a mile south of I. G. N. Railway bridge across Sycamore Creek.   [*See* page 55.]

FIGURES 4, 5.—*Raninella* (?) *starkvillensis* Rathbun, n.sp.   Dorsal and inner views of carpus of right cheliped, × 1.44, Cat. No. 73831; from Oktibbeha tongue of Selma chalk, in gullies on campus of Agricultural and Mechanical College, Starkville, Oktibbeha County, Mississippi.   [*See* page 51.]

FIGURE 6.—*Linuparus* (?) sp.   Fragment of carapace, × 1.08, Cat. No. 73843; Ripley formation, at Frisco Railroad bridge (No. 5710), 2½ miles northwest of Blue Springs, Union County, Mississippi.   [*See* page 38.]

FIGURES 7, 8.—*Pagurus banderensis* Rathbun, n.sp.   Outer and inner views of portion of right chela, × 1.44; University of Texas; from Glen Rose formation, *Salenia texana* horizon, one mile east of Bandera, Bandera County, Texas.   [*See* page 39.]

FIGURES 9–12.—*Hoploparia georgeana* Rathbun.   Lower view of left palm, upper view of same palm and finger, inner view of finger, inner view of palm, × .72, Cat. No. 73836; Monmouth formation, in an erosional exposure at Brightseat, Prince Georges County, Maryland.   [*See* page 25.]

PLATE 9

CRUSTACEA FROM THE CRETACEOUS

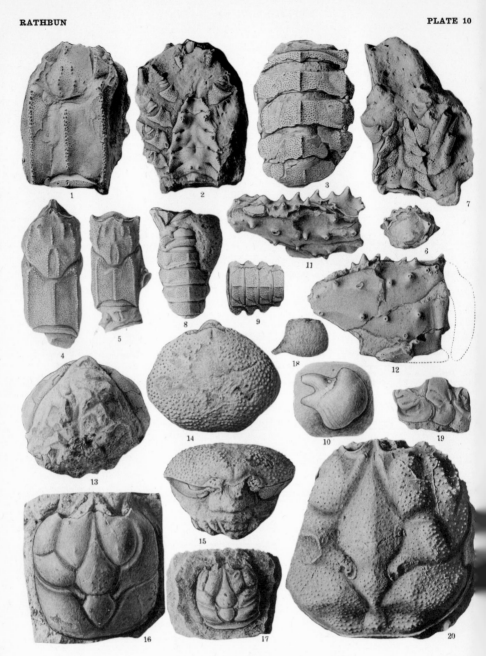

CRUSTACEA FROM THE CRETACEOUS

PLATE 10—CRUSTACEA FROM THE CRETACEOUS

FIGURES 1-3.—*Linuparus vancouverensis* (Whiteaves). Dorsal view of carapace, ventral view showing sternum and basal articles of appendages, and abdomen, first five segments, × .72, Cat. No. 73706; Marietta formation of Denison group of Comanche series, from bluff on Washita River at Frisco Railroad bridge, left bank, 2½ miles east of Platter, Bryan County, Oklahoma. [*See* page 36.]

FIGURES 4-10.—*Linuparus adkinsi* Rathbun, n.sp. Denton clay, Texas; W. S. Adkins, University of Texas. [*See* page 37.]

4.—Carapace, holotype, dorsal view, × 2.16 (284); Northern Tarrant County, southeast of Haslet and east of Blue Mound. 5, 6.—Carapace, paratype, dorsal view showing orbital spine, and front view, × 2.16 (182); about 100 yards east of 210 (see below), about 2 miles north of Denison, south of St. L. S. F. Railway track. 7.— Sternum, × 3.61 (210); Grayson County, 2 miles north of Denison and half a mile east of type-locality of Denton clay, on south side of St. L. S. F. Railway track. 8.— Abdomen, × 2.16 (182) (See above). 9.—Another abdomen showing pleura of third, fourth, and fifth segments, × 2.16 (182) (See above). 10.—Left mandible, × 5.77 (182) (See above).

FIGURES 11, 12.—*Archaeocarabus* (?) *whitfieldi* (Pilsbry). Upper and outer views of right manus, × 1.08, Cat. No. 4693, Philadelphia Academy; fingers after Pilsbry; Upper Cretaceous, Burlington County, New Jersey. [*See* page 38.]

FIGURES 13-15.—*Graptocarcinus texanus* Roemer. Ventral, dorsal, and front views of carapace, cotype, × 1.08; University of Texas; from lower part of Buda limestone at Shoal Creek, 29th Street, Austin, Travis County, Texas. [*See* page 41.]

FIGURES 16-18.—*Tetracarcinus subquadratus* Weller. [*See* page 41.]

16.—Carapace, cotype, × 2.89; New Jersey State Museum; Cliffwood clay, Cliffwood Point, New Jersey. 17.—Carapace, × 2.16, Cat. No. 73716; Lewis shale, 8 miles west of Rawlins, on Lincoln Highway (loc. 10722), Wyoming. 18.—Left palm and fixed finger, × 2.16; New Jersey State Museum; Tinton beds, Beers Hill, New Jersey.

FIGURE 19.—Macruran undetermined. Left side of 3 segments of abdomen, × 1.44; W. S. Adkins (210), University of Texas; from Denton clay, 2 miles north of Denison, Grayson County, Texas, half a mile east of Kde type-locality on south side St. L. S. F. Railway track. [*See* page 29.]

FIGURE 20.—*Dakoticancer overana* Rathbun. Carapace with basal portion of rostrum, × 2.16, Cat. No. 73840; from Ripley formation, at Whitten farm in southwest corner of southwest quarter of Sec. 21, T. 8 S., R. 4 E., Union County, Mississippi. [*See* page 40.]

PLATE 11—CRUSTACEA FROM THE CRETACEOUS

FIGURES 1–5.—*Xanthosia aspera* Rathbun. Denton clay, Grayson County, Texas; W. S. Adkins, University of Texas. [*See* page 41.] 1, 2.—Carapace and ventral view of holotype, × 2.89 (182); about 100 yards east of loc. 210, about 2 miles north of Denison, south of St. L. S. F. Railway track. 3, 4.—Front view showing orbits and dorsal view of anterior half of carapace, paratype, × 2.89; same locality as figs. 1 and 2. 5.—Fragment of carapace of largest specimen, × 2.89 (210); 2 miles north of Denison, half a mile east of Kde type-locality on south side St. L. S. F. Railway track.

FIGURES 6–8.—*Xanthosia wintoni* Rathbun. Denton clay, Grayson County, Texas; W. S. Adkins, University of Texas. [*See* page 42.] 6.—Paratype, lateral margins lacking, dorsal view, × 2.16; about 100 yards east of loc. 210, about 2 miles north of Denison, south of St. L. S. F. Railway track. 7, 8.—Holotype, front view showing basal article of antennules, and dorsal view (hinder part lacking), × 2.16; 2 miles north of Denison, half a mile east of Kde type-locality on south side St. L. S. F. Railway track.

FIGURE 9.—*Necrocarcinus oklahomensis* Rathbun, n.sp. Carapace, × 1.08, Cat. No. 73715; from Marietta formation of Denison group of Comanche series, at bluff on Washita River at Frisco Railroad bridge, left bank 2½ miles east of Platter, Bryan County, Oklahoma. [*See* page 44.]

FIGURES 10, 11.—*Dromia (?) anomala* Rathbun, n.sp. Dorsal view of carapace, × 4.33, and upper-outer view of manus, × 2.89; W. S. Adkins (210), University of Texas; from Denton clay, 2 miles north of Denison, half mile east of Kde type-locality on south side St. L. S. F. Railway track, Grayson County, Texas. [*See* page 43.]

FIGURES 12–19.—*Caloxanthus americanus* Rathbun, n.sp. Inner, outer, and upper views of right chela, × 2.89; outer view of left chela, × 2.89; upper view of right cheliped, × 3.61; dorsal, frontal, and ventral views of body, × 5.05; W. S. Adkins (209), University of Texas; from Pawpaw clay, 4½ miles southeast of Fort Worth, a quarter of a mile south of I. G. N. Railway bridge across Sycamore Creek, Tarrant County, Texas. [*See* page 56.]

FIGURES 20–22.—*Necrocarcinus texensis* Rathbun, n.sp. Texas; W. S. Adkins, University of Texas. [*See* page 45.] 20–21.—Front and dorsal views of carapace, holotype, × 2.16 (182); from Denton clay, about 100 yards east of loc. 210, about 2 miles north of Denison, south of St. L. S. F. Railway track, Grayson County. 22.—Dorsal view of carapace, paratype, × 2.16 (241); from Pawpaw clay, at Haslet station at Blue Mound, northern Tarrant County.

FIGURES 23–25.—*Necrocarcinus graysonensis* Rathbun, n.sp. Dorsal view, right profile showing orbit and front view, × 2.16; W. S. Adkins (210), University of Texas; from Denton clay, 2 miles north of Denison, half a mile east of Kde type-locality on south side St. L. S. F. Railway track. [*See* page 45.]

FIGURES 26–28.—*Prehepatus pawpawensis* Rathbun, n.sp. Outer, upper, and inner views of left chela, × 3.61; W. S. Adkins, University of Texas; from Pawpaw clay, 4 miles southwest of Fort Worth, half a mile south of Baptist Seminary, Tarrant County, Texas. [*See* page 48.]

FIGURES 29, 30.—*Prehepatus cretaceus* Rathbun, n.sp. Outer and upper views of right chela, × 2.16; W. S. Adkins (211), University of Texas; from Duck Creek limestone, 3 miles north of Denison, on south bank of Duck Creek in marl above *Pervinquieria aff. trinodosa*, Grayson County, Texas. [*See* page 47.]

FIGURE 31.—*Necrocarcinus (?)* sp. Fragment of carapace, × 1.44; W. S. Adkins (209), University of Texas; from Pawpaw clay, 4½ miles southeast of Fort Worth, a quarter of a mile south of I. G. N. Railway bridge across Sycamore Creek, Tarrant County, Texas. [*See* page 46.]

FIGURES 32, 33.—*Raninella (?) armata* Rathbun, n.sp. Flat view and left profile of segments 3–7 of abdomen, × 2.16; W. S. Adkins (284), University of Texas; from Denton clay, at Blue Mound, near Haslet, Tarrant County, Texas. [*See* page 50.]

CRUSTACEA FROM THE CRETACEOUS

CRUSTACEA FROM THE CRETACEOUS

PLATE 12—CRUSTACEA FROM THE CRETACEOUS

FIGURES 1, 2.—*Palaega williamsonensis* Rathbun, n.sp. Dorsal view and impression of same, × 2.16; from Navarro formation, 2½ miles southwest of Thrall, Williamson County, Texas. [*See* page 59.]

FIGURES 3, 4.—*Palaega guadalupensis* Rathbun, n.sp. Texas. [*See* page 59.]
3.—Dorsal view of paratype, portion of thorax, × 1.44, Cat. No. 73844; from Austin chalk, in bed of Salado Creek, one mile below crossing of Austin road, about 3.5 miles east of north of Alamo Heights, Bexar County. 4.—Dorsal view of holotype, × 1.44, Cat. No. 73845; from Taylor marl, at Guadalupe River, a few hundred yards above I. G. N. Railway bridge, one mile east of New Braunfels, Comal County.

FIGURE 5.—*Necrocarcinus pierrensis* (Rathbun). Incomplete carapace, × 2.16; Woodbury clay, Lorillard, New Jersey. [*See* page 45.]

FIGURES 6–10.—*Notopocorystes* (?) *ripleyensis* Rathbun, n.sp. Lower, inner, outer, distal, and upper views of right manus and stump of dactylus, × 2.16, Cat. No. 73792; Ripley formation, Tupelo road, one mile east of Pontotoc, Pontotoc County, Mississippi. [*See* page 49.]

FIGURES 11–13.—*Notopocorystes parvus* Rathbun, n.sp. Frontal, dorsal, and ventral views of carapace, × 2.89; W. S. Adkins (284), University of Texas; from Denton clay, at Blue Mound near Haslet, Tarrant County, Texas. [*See* page 48.]

FIGURES 14–16.—*Notopocorystes punctatus* Rathbun, n.sp. Dorsal, frontal, and ventral views of carapace, × 2.89; W. S. Adkins (210), University of Texas; from Denton clay, 2 miles north of Denison, half a mile east of Kde type-locality on south side St. L. S. F. Railway track, Grayson County, Texas. [*See* page 48.]

PLATE 13—CRUSTACEA FROM THE CRETACEOUS

FIGURES 1–5.—*Ophthalmoplax comancheensis* Rathbun, n.gen. and sp.   Texas; W. S. Adkins, University of Texas.   [*See* page 54.]

1, 2.—Upper and outer views of dactyl of right cheliped, × 1.44 (244); from Pawpaw clay, in Sycamore Creek valley, ±4½ miles southeast of Fort Worth and half a mile northeast of loc. 209, Tarrant County.   3–5.—Prehensile and outer views of left fixed finger and outer view of left movable finger, × 1.44 (211); from 3 miles north of Denison, south bank of Duck Creek, 40 feet above base of Kde type-locality, in marl above *Pervinquieria aff. trinodosa*, Grayson County.

FIGURE 6.—*Necrocarcinus* (?) sp.   Fragment of carapace, × 2.16; W. S. Adkins (209), University of Texas; from Pawpaw clay, 4½ miles southeast of Fort Worth, a quarter of a mile south of I. G. N. Railway bridge across Sycamore Creek, Tarrant County, Texas.   [*See* page 46.]

FIGURES 7, 8.—*Menippe cretacea* Rathbun, n.sp.   Outer views of dactyl and fixed finger (holotype) of right cheliped, × .72, Cat. No. 73827; Woodbine formation at Timber Creek, 4 miles due west of Lewisville, Denton County, Texas, and a few hundred yards below a road bridge.   [*See* page 57.]

FIGURES 9–12.—*Stenocionops primus* Rathbun, n.sp.   Upper, inner, outer, and distal views of right manus, × 1.08, Cat. No. 73838; from bed of glauconitic sand in Brownstown formation, on old road half a mile south of Buckrange, Howard County, Arkansas.   [*See* page 58.]

FIGURES 13–18.—*Ophthalmoplax stephensoni* Rathbun, n.sp.   [*See* page 52.]

13, 14.—Dorsal and ventral views of holotype, × .72, Cat. No. 73793; from Ripley formation, near base of sector, loose in ravine, on land of J. A. Roberts, 5½ miles east of New Albany and a few rods north of New Albany and Baldwin road at "The Caves," Union County, Mississippi.   15.—Outer view, pair of fingers, × 1.08, Cat. No. 73795; from Ripley formation, in cut of Louisville and Nashville Railroad, 1⅞ miles north of Fort Deposit, Lowndes County, Alabama.   16, 17.—Outer and inner views of left chela of holotype, × 1.08, Cat. No. 73793 (See above, figs. 13, 14). 18.—Outer view of left chela, × 1.08, Cat. No. 73794; from Peedee formation, at Davis Landing, right bank, Peedee River, Florence County, South Carolina.

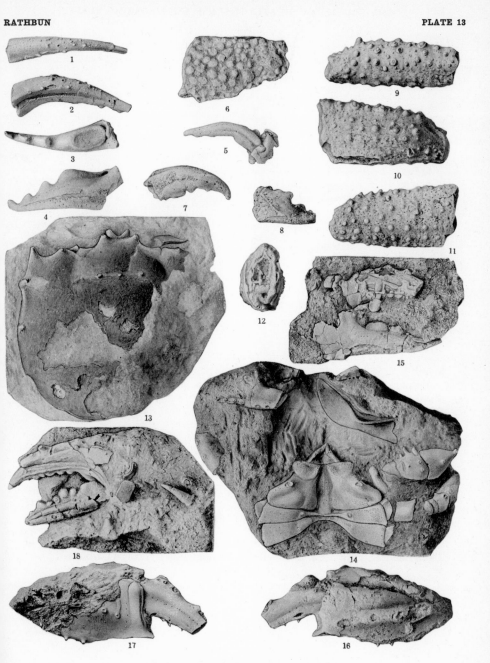

CRUSTACEA FROM THE CRETACEOUS

CRUSTACEA FROM THE EOCENE AND *RANINELLA* FROM THE CRETACEOUS

PLATE 14—CRUSTACEA FROM THE EOCENE AND *Raninella* FROM THE CRETACEOUS

FIGURES 1-6.—*Ischnodactylus cookei* Rathbun, n.sp.   [*See* page 63.]

1-4.—Upper (× 2.89) and outer (× 1.44) views of right manus and fixed finger of holotype, and outer and lower views (× 2.16) of right manus and fixed finger of paratype, Cat. No. 371512; from Sucarnoochee beds, Midway, in Prairie Creek region, Wilcox County, Alabama.   5, 6.—Prehensile and opposite views of fragment of finger, × 3.61; Alabama Museum of Natural History; from Sucarnoochee beds, at Estelle, Wilcox County, Alabama.

FIGURES 7-12.—*Ischnodactylus cultellus* Rathbun, n.sp.   [*See* page 64.]

7-9.—Upper, lower, and outer views of dactylus of left cheliped, holotype, × 2.16; Alabama Museum of Natural History; from Sucarnoochee beds at Estelle, Wilcox County, Alabama.   10-12.—Lower, upper, and outer views of right propodal finger, × 2.16; Johns Hopkins University; from Dry Creek, Jackson, Hinds County, Mississippi (horizon not given).

FIGURES 13-18.—*Paguristes johnsoni* Rathbun, n.sp.   Lower, upper, distal, and outer views of right major palm, holotype, × 1.44, Cat. No. 371705, and upper and outer views of left minor chela, × 2.16, Cat. No. 371706; from Sucarnoochee beds, Prairie Creek and Pine Barren section, Wilcox County, Alabama.   [*See* page 78.]

FIGURES 19-22.—*Ischnodactylus* (?) *dentatus* Rathbun, n.sp.   Lower, outer, and inner views of right propodal finger, holotype, × 3.61, and inner view of same finger of paratype, × 3.61; Johns Hopkins University; from lower Eocene at Dry Creek, Jackson, Hinds County, Mississippi.   [*See* page 65.]

FIGURES 23, 24.—*Ischnodactylus* (?) sp.   Outer and distal views of right manus (incomplete), × 2.89, Cat. No. 371514; from Sucarnoochee beds, Prairie Creek, Wilcox County, Alabama.   [*See* page 66.]

FIGURES 25-31.—*Hoploparia johnsoni* Rathbun, n.sp.   Outer view of left palm, for surface, × 1.44, Cat. No. 371520; inner view of basal portion of dactylus of right cheliped, showing tubercles, × 2.89; Cat. No. 371520; left profile of smaller carapace and abdomen, showing pleura, × 1.44, Cat. No. 371518; left profile of larger carapace and abdomen, holotype, × 1.08, Cat. No. 371518; outer view of right propodal finger, × 1.44, Cat. No. 371520; outer view of right palm with finger, × 1.08, Cat. No. 371520; inner view of largest palm (right), × 1.08, Cat. No. 371520; from Sucarnoochee beds, at Prairie Creek and Pine Barren section, Wilcox County, Alabama.   [*See* page 61.]

FIGURES 32, 33.—*Raninella mucronata* Rathbun, n.sp.   Dorsal and ventral views of holotype, × 4.33; W. S. Adkins (284), University of Texas; Denton clay, at Blue Mound near Haslet, Tarrant County, Texas.   [*See* page 50.]

PLATE 15—CRUSTACEA FROM THE EOCENE

FIGURES 1–3, 5, 6.—*Callianassa ulrichi* C. A. White. [*See* page 71.]
1–3.—Inner and outer views of left chela, × 1.44, and outer view of right propodus (incomplete) and fixed finger, × 2.16, Cat. No. 8910; from Clayton limestone, at Johnson's Well, top of Capitol Hill, corner of Battery and 9th streets, station 2218, Hayden Survey, Little Rock, Pulaski County, Arkansas. 5–6.—Outer views of right and left movable fingers, × 2.16, Cat. No. 8910 (See above, figs. 1–3).

FIGURE 4. *Callianassa ulrichi claibornensis* Rathbun, n.subsp.   Outer view of left propodal finger, × 2.16, Cat. No. 371588; of Claiborne age; from east bank of Chickasawhay River about half a mile below Enterprise, Clarke County, Mississippi. [*See* page 72.]

FIGURES 7–10.—*Callianassa alabamensis* Rathbun, n.sp.   Distal and outer views of right chela, holotype, × 1.08, and outer and upper views of dactylus of right cheliped, paratype, × 1.44, Cat. No. 371505; from Sucarnoochee beds, at Prairie Creek, Wilcox County, Alabama. [*See* page 70.]

FIGURES 11–14.—*Callianassa beta* Rathbun, n.sp.   Inner, outer, upper, and distal views, of left manus, × 2.16, Cat. No. 371507; Sucarnoochee beds, Pine Barren section, Wilcox County, Alabama. [*See* page 68.]

FIGURES 15–18.—*Callianassa epsilon* Rathbun, n.sp.   Upper, outer, inner, and distal views of left manus, × 2.16, Cat. No. 371510; Sucarnoochee beds, Prairie Creek region, Wilcox County, Alabama. [*See* page 69.]

FIGURES 19–22.—*Callianassa delta* Rathbun, n.sp.   Inner, outer, upper, and distal views of right manus and piece of finger, × 1.44, Cat. No. 371509; Sucarnoochee beds, Prairie Creek, Wilcox County, Alabama. [*See* page 69.]

FIGURES 23–25, 27.—*Callianassa alpha* Rathbun, n.sp.   [*See* page 67.]
23–25.—Upper, outer, and inner views of propodus of right cheliped, holotype, × 2.16, Cat. No. 371506; Sucarnoochee beds, Prairie Creek, Wilcox County, Alabama. 27.—Outer view of broken palm and finger, showing characteristic excrescence at base of finger, × 2.89, Cat. No. 371506 (See above, figs. 23–25).

FIGURES 26, 28, 29.—*Callianassa alpha* Rathbun, n. var.   [*See* page 67.]
26.—Inner view of left palm, × 2.16, Cat. No. 371572; Jackson formation, in large ravine below old reservoir at Yazoo City, about one mile south of Y. and M. V. R. R. station along street-car line, Yazoo County, Mississippi. 28–29.—Dorsal view of telson and right profile of abdomen showing punctae on middle segments, × 2.16, Cat. No. 371573 (See above, with 371572).

FIGURES 30–35.—*Callianassa hulli* Rathbun, n.sp.   Outer, inner, and distal views of right manus, holotype, × 3.61; inner view of right chela embedded in nodule, × 3.61; outer view of lower part of wrist, × 7.2; and inner view of immovable finger embedded, × 7.2, Cat. No. 371576; from the Midway, at Buzzard Bluff, Miller County, Sec. 16, T. 14 S., R. 26 W., Arkansas. [*See* page 72.]

CRUSTACEA FROM THE EOCENE

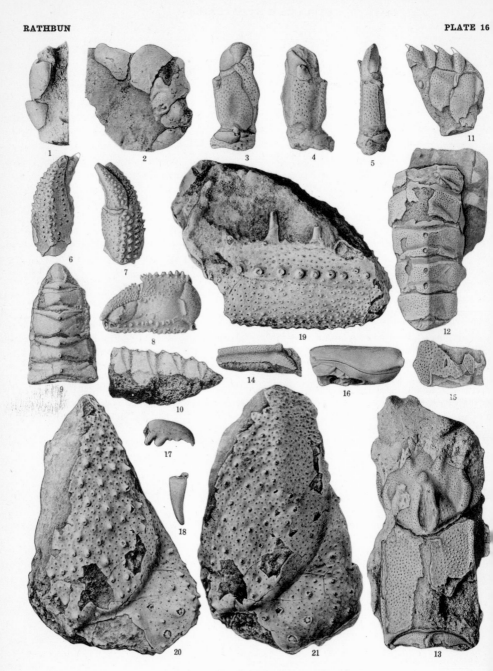

CRUSTACEA FROM THE EOCENE

PLATE 16—CRUSTACEA FROM THE EOCENE

FIGURES 1, 2.—*Upogebia midwayensis* Rathbun, n.sp. Right profile of segments 6–7 and left profile of segments 2–6 of abdomen, × 1.44, Cat. No. 371516; from Sucarnoochee beds in Pine Barren section, Wilcox County, Alabama. [*See* page 66.]

FIGURES 3–5.—*Nephrops midwayensis* Rathbun, n.sp. Inner, outer, and upper views of left chela, × 1.44, Cat. No. 371741; from Sucarnoochee beds in Pine Barren section, Wilcox County, Alabama. [*See* page 62.]

FIGURES 6–8.—*Pagurus alabamensis* Rathbun, n.sp. Lower, upper, and inner views of right chela, × 2.89, Cat. No. 371703; from Sucarnoochee beds in Prairie Creek, Wilcox County, Alabama. [*See* page 78.]

FIGURES 9, 10.—*Linuparus texanus* Rathbun, n.sp. Dorsal view and left profile of abdomen, × 1.08, Cat. No. 371390; from the Midway of Dimmit County, Texas. [*See* page 73.]

FIGURES 11–14.—*Linuparus wilcoxensis* Rathbun, n.sp. Profile of fragment of abdomen to show median spines pointing forward, × 1.44; dorsal view of abdomen, × 1.44; dorsal view of carapace, holotype, × 1.08; and profile of fragment of carapace showing spine behind cervical suture, × 1.44, Cat. No. 371499; from Sucarnoochee beds, Prairie Creek, Wilcox County, Alabama. [*See* page 74.]

FIGURE 15.—*Linuparus* (?) sp. Fragment of carapace, × 1.44; W. S. Adkins (209), University of Texas; from Pawpaw clay, 4½ miles southeast of Fort Worth, a quarter of a mile south of I. G. N. Railway bridge across Sycamore Creek, Tarrant County, Texas. [*See* page 38.]

FIGURE 16.—*Notosceles bournei* Rathbun. Right profile of carapace and sternum, × 2.89, Cat. No. 371696; from the Midway, at Black Bluff, Tombigbee River, Sumter County, Alabama. [*See* page 82.]

FIGURES 17, 18.—*Panopeus estellensis* Rathbun, n.sp. Outer and upper views of right major dactyl, × 2.16; Alabama Museum of Natural History; from Sucarnoochee beds, at Estelle, Wilcox County, Alabama. [*See* page 93.]

FIGURES 19–21.—*Archaeocarabus* (?) *gardnerae* Rathbun, n.sp. Side view of left palm, × 1.08, and dorsal view and right profile of portion of hinder half of carapace, × 1.08, Cat. No. 371515; from the Midway, at Black Bluff, Tombigbee River, Sumter County, Alabama. [*See* page 75.]

PLATE 17—CRUSTACEA FROM THE EOCENE

FIGURES 1–6.—*Dromilites americana* Rathbun, n.sp. [*See* page 79.]

1, 2.—Ventral view of 2 specimens for antennules, × 2.16, and sternum, × 1.44, Cat. No. 371688; from Sucarnoochee beds, from Prairie Creek and Allenton, Wilcox County, Alabama. 3.—Dorsal view of carapace, × 1.44, Cat. No. 371687; Sucarnoochee beds, from Prairie Creek and Pine Barren section, Wilcox County, Alabama. 4.—Dorsal view of carapace for ornamentation, × 2.16; from Black Bluff, Tombigbee River, Sumter County, Alabama. 5.—Dorsal view of carapace, holotype, × 1.44, Cat. No. 371687 (See above). 6.—Outer view of carpus and propodus of left cheliped, × 2.16, Cat. No. 371688 (See above).

FIGURES 7–10.—*Callianassa gamma* Rathbun, n.sp. Outer, inner, lower, and distal views of left manus, × 2.16, Cat. No. 371508; from Sucarnoochee beds, at Prairie Creek, Wilcox County, Alabama. [*See* page 68.]

FIGURE 11.—*Hepatiscus americanus* Rathbun, n.sp. Dorsal view of carapace, × 2.16, Cat. No. 371695; from Sucarnoochee beds, at Prairie Creek, Wilcox County, Alabama. [*See* page 80.]

FIGURES 12–17.—*Symethis johnsoni*, Rathbun, n.sp. [*See* page 83.]

12.—Ventral view for sternum, × 1.44, Cat. No. 371691; Sucarnoochee beds, Prairie Creek and Pine Barren section, Wilcox County, Alabama. 13.—Dorsal view of carapace, holotype, × 1.44, Cat. No. 371705; same horizon as 12, Prairie Creek and Allenton, Alabama. 14–16.—Carapace with rostrum, × 1.44, and dorsal and ventral views of carapace and abdomen, × 3.61, Cat. No. 371691 (See above). 17.—Carapace showing orbital spine, × 2.89, Cat. No. 371693; same place as figure 13.

PLATE 17

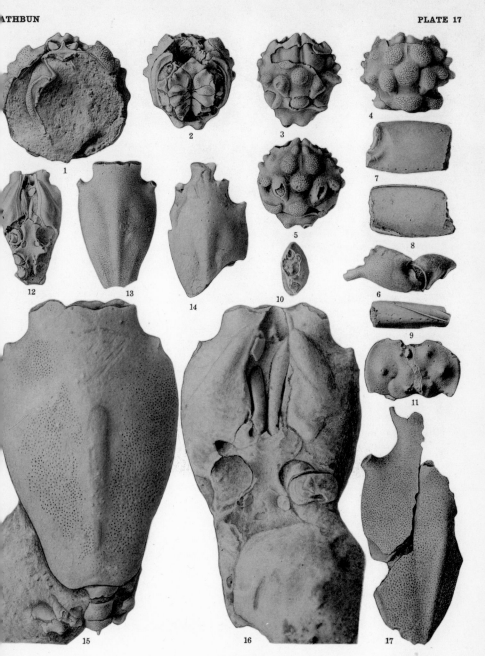

CRUSTACEA FROM THE EOCENE

PLATE 18

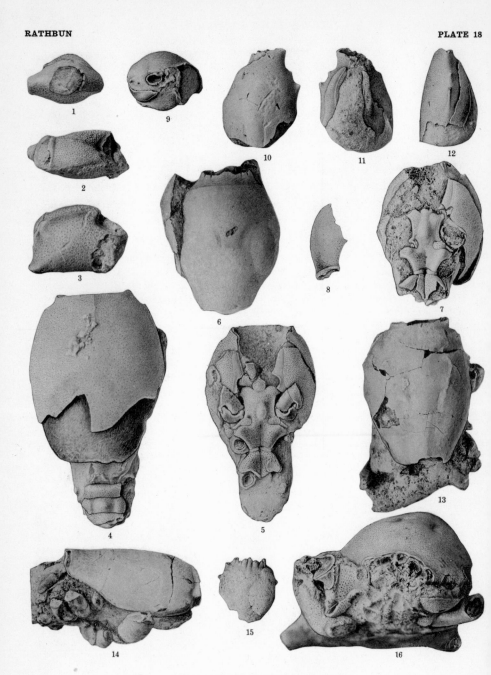

CRUSTACEA FROM THE EOCENE

PLATE 18—CRUSTACEA FROM THE EOCENE

FIGURES 1–8.—*Raninoides ovalis* Rathbun, n.sp. Sucarnoochee beds, Wilcox County, Alabama. [*See* page 81.]

1–3.—Distal, upper, and outer views of left palm, × 4.33, Cat. No. 371501; Prairie Creek and Allenton. 4, 5.—Dorsal view of carapace and portion of abdomen, × 2.89, and ventral view showing sternum, × 2.16, Cat. No. 371692; Prairie Creek and Pine Barren section. 6–8.—Dorsal view of carapace showing frontal teeth, × 2.16; ventral view of a second specimen, × 1.44; and carpus of left cheliped, × 2.89; from same place as figures 1–3.

FIGURES 9–12.—*Symnista bidentata* Rathbun, n.sp. Front view showing orbit, dorsal, ventral, and right profile, × 2.89, Cat. No. 371742; from Sucarnoochee beds, Prairie Creek and Allenton, Wilcox County, Alabama. [*See* page 84.]

FIGURES 13–16.—*Raninella eocenica* Rathbun, n.sp. Sucarnoochee beds, Wilcox County, Alabama. [*See* page 82.]

13, 14.—Dorsal view and right profile of holotype, × 2.16, Cat. No. 371701; Prairie Creek. 15.—Dorsal view of carapace showing dentation, × 1.08, Cat. No. 371700; Prairie Creek and Pine Barren section. 16.—Front view for orbits, × 2.89, Cat. No. 371701 (See above).

PLATE 19—CRUSTACEA FROM THE EOCENE

FIGURES 1–11.—*Menippe burnsi* Rathbun, n.sp.   [*See* page 85.]

1–6.—Upper and outer views of right manus, × .72; outer view of left manus, × .72; inner, outer, and lower views of second left manus, × 1.44, Cat. No. 371580; from Castle Hayne marl, Jackson formation, at city quarry near cemetery, Wilmington, New Hanover County, North Carolina.   7–8.—Prehensile and outer views of right movable finger, × 1.44, Cat. No. 371581; from Santee limestone, basal Jackson formation, on Belle Broughton plantation, half a mile southeast of Creston, Calhoun County, South Carolina, on branch of Halfway Swamp.   9–11.—Inner and outer views of carpus-propodus of right cheliped, and outer view of right manus, × .72, Cat. No. 371580 (See figs. 1–6).

FIGURES 12–15.—*Menippe anomala* Rathbun, n.sp.   Outer, proximal, upper, and inner views of right manus, × 1.44, Cat. No. 371524; from Castle Hayne marl, Jackson formation, in city quarry near cemetery, Wilmington, New Hanover County, North Carolina.   [*See* page 87.]

FIGURE 16.—*Menippe jacksonensis* Rathbun, n.sp.   Inner view, right minor chela, × 2.16, Cat. No. 371589; from Jackson formation, from bluff on the west side of Tom Creek, Jackson, 200 feet south of Rankin Street and 800 ± feet west of South State Street, Mississippi.   [*See* page 86.]

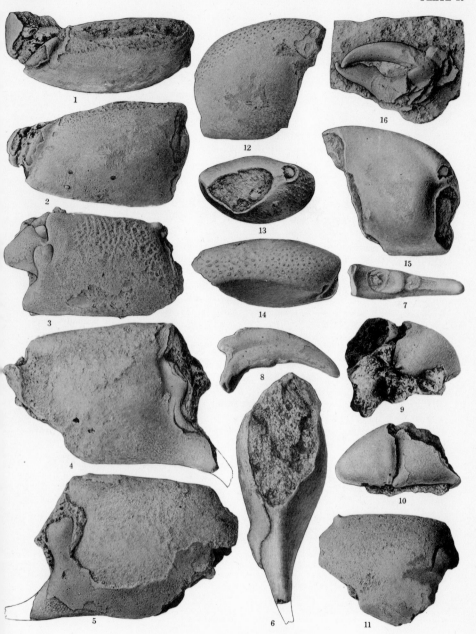

CRUSTACEA FROM THE EOCENE

PLATE 20

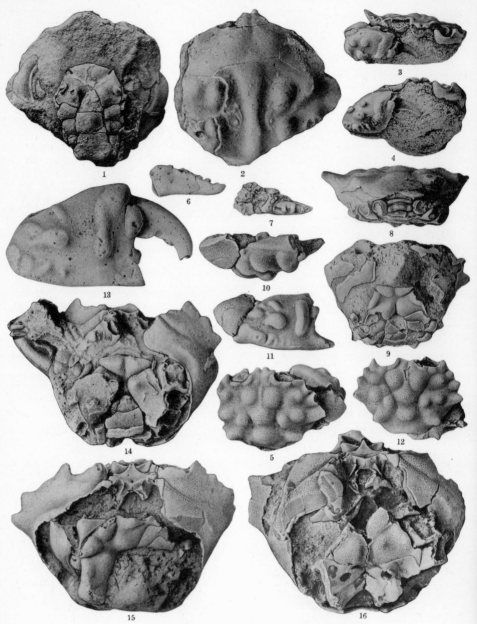

CRUSTACEA FROM THE EOCENE

PLATE 20—CRUSTACEA FROM THE EOCENE

FIGURES 1, 2.—*Zanthopsis carolinensis* Rathbun, n.sp. Ventral view showing sternum and abdomen, and dorsal view of carapace, × .72, Cat. No. 371586; from lower Claiborne, at Creston, Orangeburg County, South Carolina. [*See* page 90.]

FIGURES 3–16.—*Xanthilites alabamensis* Rathbun, n.sp. Frontal, ventral, and dorsal views of holotype, × 1.44, Cat. No. 371708; outer and prehensile views of fixed finger, × 1.44, Cat. No. 371690; posterior and ventral views of paratype, × 2.16, Cat. No. 371708; upper and outer views of right carpus and propodus of cheliped, × 2.16, Cat. No. 371690; dorsal view for detail (284), × 2.16, Cat. No. 371707; outer view of right major palm with dactylus, × 2.16, Cat. No. 371690; ventral view of ♀, × 2.16, Cat. No. 371708; ventral view showing antennal and antennular articles (284), × 2.89, Cat. No. 371707; and ventral view showing maxilliped, × 2.16, Cat. No. 371708; all from Sucarnoochee beds at Prairie Creek (264) or Pine Barren section (284), Wilcox County, Alabama. [*See* page 91.[

PLATE 21—CRUSTACEA FROM THE EOCENE AND THE OLIGOCENE

FIGURES 1–3.—*Stenocionops suwanneeana* Rathbun, n.sp.   Outer, upper, and distal views, × 1.08, Cat. No. 137885; from Ocala limestone, Eocene, at Rowland's Bluff, Suwannee County, Florida. [*See* page 95.]

FIGURES 4–6.—*Callinectes alabamensis* Rathbun, n.sp.   Distal, upper, and outer views of left manus, × 1.44; Johns Hopkins University; from Byram marl (?), Vicksburg group, at Perdue Hill, Monroe County, Alabama. [*See* page 98.]

FIGURES 7–8.—*Ranina georgiana* Rathbun, n.sp.   Right profile and dorsal view of carapace, × 1.08, Cat. No. 371714; from Glendon limestone, Vicksburg group, at old factory about 1½ miles above Bainbridge, Decatur County, Georgia. [*See* page 97.]

FIGURES 9–11.—*Harpactocarcinus mississippiensis* Rathbun, n.sp.   Frontal, dorsal, and ventral views of ♀, × .72, Cat. No. 371577; from Jackson formation, in large ravine below old reservoir at Yazoo City about one mile south of the Y. and M. V. R. R. station, along street-car line, Yazoo County, Mississippi. [*See* page 88.]

FIGURES 12–14.—*Callianassa berryi* Rathbun, n.sp.   Distal, outer, and inner views of left manus, × 1.44; Johns Hopkins University; from Glendon limestone, Vicksburg group, at Vicksburg, Warren County, Mississippi. [*See* page 96.]

FIGURES 15–17.—*Zanthopsis errans* Woods.   Distal, upper, and outer views of right manus, outer layer fragmentary, × 1.08, Cat. No. 139148; from Wahtubbee horizon, lower Claiborne, from Clarke County, Mississippi. [*See* page 90.]

FIGURE 18.—*Scyllarella aspera* Rathbun, n.gen. and sp.   Carapace behind cervical suture and first segment of abdomen, × .72, Cat. No. 371503; from Sucarnoochee beds, at Prairie Creek and Pine Barren section, Wilcox County, Alabama. [*See* page 77.]

FIGURES 19–22.—*Galenopsis americana* Rathbun, n.sp.   Distal, upper, outer, and inner views of right palm, × 2.16, Cat. No. 371743; from the Midway of the Pine Barren region, Wilcox County, Alabama. [*See* page 93.]

FIGURE 23.—*Plagiolophus bakeri* Rathbun, n.sp.   Dorsal view of carapace, × 1.44, Cat. No. 371574; from Cooks Mountain stage of lower Claiborne of the horizon of the Moseley Ferry beds, at Moseley's Ferry, northwestern Brazos County, Texas. [*See* page 94.]

PLATE 21

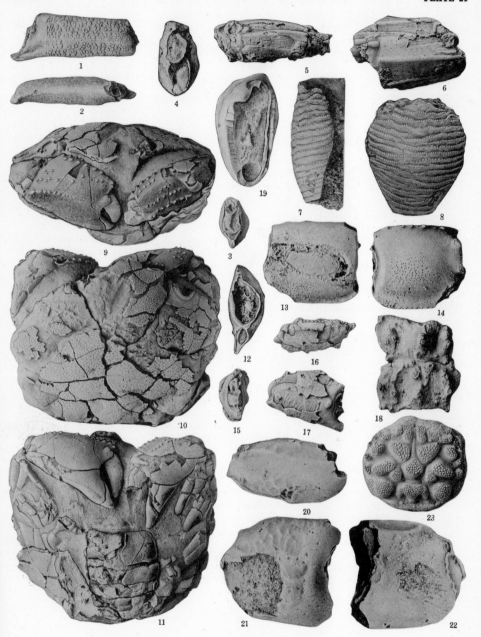

CRUSTACEA FROM THE EOCENE AND THE OLIGOCENE

CRUSTACEA FROM THE OLIGOCENE AND THE MIOCENE

PLATE 22—CRUSTACEA FROM THE OLIGOCENE AND THE MIOCENE

FIGURES 1–6.—*Menippe floridana* Rathbun, n.sp. Choctawhatchee marl, Florida. [*See* page 109.]

1–4.—Inner, outer, upper, and prehensile views of left movable finger, × 1.08, Cat. No. 371718; from Harveys Creek, Leon County. 5, 6.—Inner and prehensile views of right immovable finger, × 1.44, Cat. No. 371719.

FIGURES 7–11.—*Necronectes vaughani* Rathbun, n.sp. [*See* page 99.]

7.—Dorsal view of carapace, × .72; Johns Hopkins University; from Glendon limestone at Vicksburg, Warren County, Mississippi. 8.—Ventral view showing maxilliped, × .72, Cat. No. 371728; from Glendon limestone, on hard ledge at Glass Bayou, Vicksburg. 9.—Dorsal view of carapace, holotype, × .72; Johns Hopkins University. 10.—Ventral view showing carapace and sternum, × .72, Cat. No. 371728. 11.—Ventral view showing cheliped and sternum, × .72; Johns Hopkins University.

FIGURES 12, 13.—*Necronectes drydeni* Rathbun, n.sp. Dorsal and ventral views of holotype, × .72; Johns Hopkins University; from Choptank formation, on a float about 100 feet south of Calvert Beach, probably from "zone 17," Maryland. [*See* page 107.]

PLATE 23—CRUSTACEA FROM THE MIOCENE

FIGURES 1–5.—*Archaeoplax signifera* Stimpson. From greensand layer, upper Miocene, on Marthas Vineyard, Dukes County, Massachusetts. [*See* page 112.]

1, 2.—Upper view of right ambulatory legs lacking extremities, × 1.44, Cat. No. 371424, and outer maxilliped, × 2.16, Cat. No. 371428; from Gay Head cliffs. 3, 4.—Carapace and ventral view of sternum and bases of legs, × 1.08, Cat. No. 371430; from Weyquosque Cliffs (eastern marl bed). 5.—Outer view of left chela, × 1.44, Cat. No. 371424; from Gay Head cliffs.

FIGURE 6.—*Petrochirus inequalis* Rathbun. Outer view of tip of left propodal finger, × 2.16, Cat. No. 371466; from Chipola formation on north bank of Tenmile Creek at wagon bridge on road from Forestville to Marianna, probably about 20 miles from Marianna, Calhoun County, Florida. [*See* page 104.]

FIGURES 7, 8.—*Scylla floridana* Rathbun, n.sp. Cross-section of distal end of palm, and outer view of fingers of right chela, × .72, Cat. No. 371717; near top of Tampa limestone, on east bank of Apalachicola River along Florida Road No. 1, Chattahoochee, Gadsden County, Florida. [*See* page 108.]

FIGURES 9, 10.—*Lobonotus foerstei* Rathbun, n.sp. Carapace and ventral surface showing sternum and basal article of cheliped, × 1.44, Cat. No. 371431; from greensand layer, upper Miocene, at Gay Head cliffs, Marthas Vineyard, Dukes County, Massachusetts. [*See* page 110.]

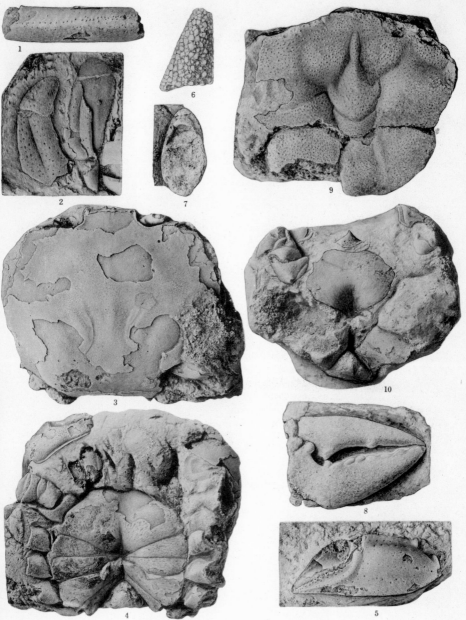

CRUSTACEA FROM THE MIOCENE

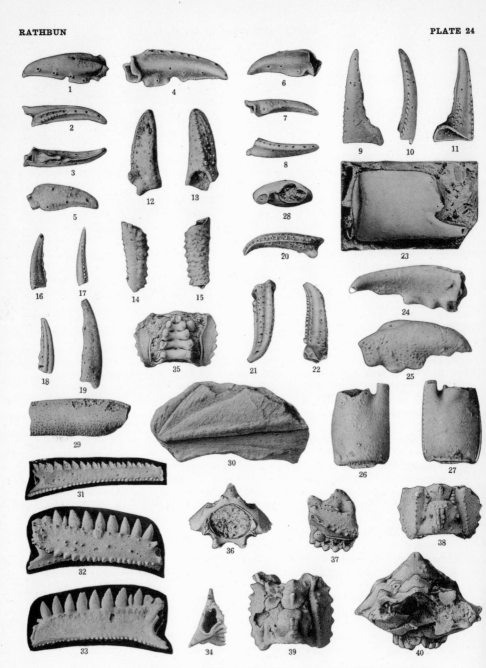

CRUSTACEA FROM THE EOCENE, THE MIOCENE, AND THE PLIOCENE

PLATE 24—CRUSTACEA FROM THE EOCENE, THE MIOCENE, AND THE PLIOCENE

FIGURES 1–11.—*Callianassa floridana* Rathbun, n.sp. Outer, upper, and lower views of left major dactyl, holotype, × 2.16; inner view of largest left major dactyl, × 2.16; outer, inner, lower, and upper views of right minor dactyl, × 2.89; outer, lower, and inner views of left fixed finger, × 2.16; Cat. No. 371469; from Chipola formation, Alum Bluff group, lower bed of calcareous red sand, on Apalachicola River, Liberty County, Florida. [*See* page 100.]

FIGURES 12–15.—*Paguristes chipolensis* Rathbun, n.sp. Inner and outer views of dactylus of right chela, holotype, × 3.61, and inner and outer views of propodus of right ambulatory leg, × 3.61, Cat. No. 371465; from Chipola formation, Alum Bluff group, one mile below Bailey's Ferry on Chipola River, from banks of river above white limestone bed, Calhoun County, Florida. [*See* page 105.]

FIGURES 16–19.—*Euprognatha*, sp. Inner, prehensile, and outer views of dactyl of left chela, and outer view of a dactyl of a larger worn left chela, × 2.89, Cat. No. 371715; from upper Miocene, at Hosford [formerly Coes Mill], Liberty County, Florida. [*See* page 112.]

FIGURES 20–22.—*Callianassa suffolkensis* Rathbun, n.sp. Upper, outer, and inner views of right movable finger, × 2.89, Cat. No. 166064; from Yorktown formation, 3 miles northeast of Suffolk, Nansemond County, Virginia. [*See* page 103.]

FIGURES 23–28.—*Callianassa matsoni* Rathbun, n.sp. Florida. [*See* page 102.]

23.—Outer view right palm and fixed finger, holotype, × 1.44, Cat. No. 371470; Chipola formation, Sopchoppy, Wakulla County. 24.—Inner view, right movable finger, × 5.05, Cat. No. 371464; Chipola formation, spring on left bank of Suwannee River about 100 yards above Rock Island and about half a mile above White Springs; No. 3 of section; Columbia County. 25–28.—Outer view of right movable finger, × 5.05, and outer, inner, and distal views of right palm, × 2.16, Cat. No. 371463; exact locality not given.

FIGURE 29.—Family Xanthidae, genus and species undetermined. Outer view of merus of left ambulatory leg, × 1.08; Alabama Museum of Natural History; from lower Eocene, Pine Barren Creek, Wilcox County, Alabama. [*See* page 94.]

FIGURE 30.—*Portunus* sp. Distal portion of fingers, × 1.08, Cat. No. 371892; from Tampa limestone at Aspalaga Bluff, Apalachicola River, about 10 feet above river level, Gadsden County, Florida. [*See* page 107.]

FIGURES 31–34.—*Parthenope (Platylambrus) charlottensis* Rathbun, n.sp. Lower, outer, inner, and distal views of propodus of left cheliped, × 1.08, Cat. No. 371716; from Caloosahatchee beds at Alligator Creek, Willcox, Charlotte County, Florida. [*See* page 114.]

FIGURES 35–40.—*Scyllarella gibbera* Rathbun, n.sp. Ventral, posterior, and left profile views of carapace and sternum and dorsal view of carapace, lacking anterior portion, holotype, and dorsal and anterior views, showing right orbital and antennular cavities of carapace, paratype, × 1.44, Cat. No. 371502; from Sucarnooc hee beds at Prairie Creek, Wilcox County, Alabama. [*See* page 76.]

PLATE 25—CRUSTACEA FROM THE CRETACEOUS

FIGURES 1–3.—*Linuparus kleinfelderi* Rathbun.   Left profile and dorsal view, also plaster cast made from mold of figure 2; from Upper Cretaceous, at Great Neck, Long Island; specimen, including mold, in Museum of Comparative Zoölogy, Harvard University; plaster cast in U. S. National Museum.   [*See* page 35.]

CRUSTACEA FROM THE CRETACEOUS

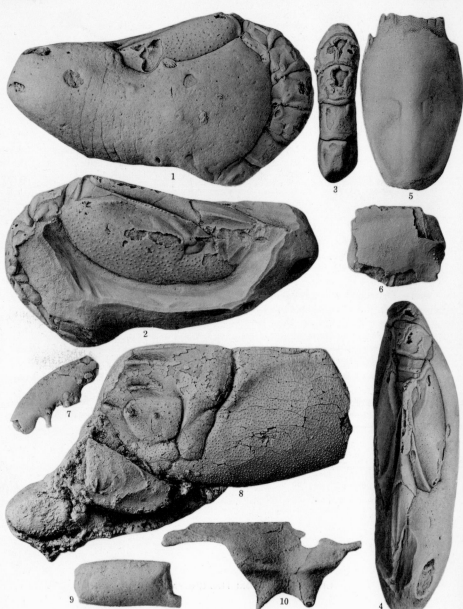

CRUSTACEA FROM THE CRETACEOUS AND THE OLIGOCENE-MIOCENE

PLATE 26—CRUSTACEA FROM THE CRETACEOUS AND THE OLIGOCENE-MIOCENE

FIGURES 1–4.—*Meyeria mexicana* Rathbun, n.sp. Holotype; from Lower Cretaceous, Chihuahua, Mexico. [*See* page 17.]

1.—Left side, especially of the tail, × 1.44. 2.—Right side, × 1.44. 3.—Dorsal view of tail end, × 1.44. 4.—Dorsal view, the carapace pointing downward, × 1.44.

FIGURE 5.—*Notosceles bournei* Rathbun. Dorsal view, × 1.44; from Navarro group, Bastrop County, Texas. [*See* page 51.]

FIGURES 6, 7.—*Callianassa vaughani* Rathbun. From Upper Oligocene-Miocene, Tamaulipas, Mexico. [*See* page 104.]

6.—Left manus, inner side, × 1.44. 7.—Left movable finger, outer side, × 1.44.

FIGURE 8.—*Hoploparia tennesseensis* Rathbun. Left side view, × 1.44; from Ripley formation, Coon Creek, Tennessee. [*See* page 25.]

FIGURE 9.—*Callianassa bosqueana*, n.sp. Right manus, outer surface, × 2.16; Comanche Peak formation, Bosque County, Texas. [*See* page 34.]

FIGURE 10.—*Ophthalmoplax stephensoni*, n.sp. Frontal teeth viewed from in front, × 3.61; Upper Cretaceous, Maverick County, Texas. [*See* page 52.]

INDEX